# INTERNATIONAL
# WILDLIFE
## ENCYCLOPEDIA

### THIRD EDITION

### Volume 2
### BAR–BRO

Marshall Cavendish Corporation
99 White Plains Road
Tarrytown, New York 10591–9001

Website: www.marshallcavendish.com

Library of Congress Cataloging-in-Publication Data

Burton, Maurice, 1898-
    International wildlife encyclopedia / [Maurice Burton, Robert Burton] .-- 3rd ed.
       p. cm.
    Includes bibliographical references (p.).
    Contents: v. 1. Aardvark - barnacle goose -- v. 2. Barn owl - brow-antlered deer -- v. 3. Brown bear - cheetah -- v. 4. Chickaree - crabs -- v. 5. Crab spider - ducks and geese -- v. 6. Dugong - flounder -- v. 7. Flowerpecker - golden mole -- v. 8. Golden oriole - hartebeest -- v. 9. Harvesting ant - jackal -- v. 10. Jackdaw - lemur -- v. 11. Leopard - marten -- v. 12. Martial eagle - needlefish -- v. 13. Newt - paradise fish -- v. 14. Paradoxical frog - poorwill -- v. 15. Porbeagle - rice rat -- v. 16. Rifleman - sea slug -- v. 17. Sea snake - sole -- v. 18. Solenodon - swan -- v. 19. Sweetfish - tree snake -- v. 20. Tree squirrel - water spider -- v. 21. Water vole - zorille -- v. 22. Index volume.
    ISBN 0-7614-7266-5 (set) -- ISBN 0-7614-7267-3 (v. 1) -- ISBN 0-7614-7268-1 (v. 2) -- ISBN 0-7614-7269-X (v. 3) -- ISBN 0-7614-7270-3 (v. 4) -- ISBN 0-7614-7271-1 (v. 5) -- ISBN 0-7614-7272-X (v. 6) -- ISBN 0-7614-7273-8 (v. 7) -- ISBN 0-7614-7274-6 (v. 8) -- ISBN 0-7614-7275-4 (v. 9) -- ISBN 0-7614-7276-2 (v. 10) -- ISBN 0-7614-7277-0 (v. 11) -- ISBN 0-7614-7278-9 (v. 12) -- ISBN 0-7614-7279-7 (v. 13) -- ISBN 0-7614-7280-0 (v. 14) -- ISBN 0-7614-7281-9 (v. 15) -- ISBN 0-7614-7282-7 (v. 16) -- ISBN 0-7614-7283-5 (v. 17) -- ISBN 0-7614-7284-3 (v. 18) -- ISBN 0-7614-7285-1 (v. 19) -- ISBN 0-7614-7286-X (v. 20) -- ISBN 0-7614-7287-8 (v. 21) -- ISBN 0-7614-7288-6 (v. 22)
    1. Zoology -- Dictionaries.    I. Burton, Robert, 1941-   . II. Title.

    QL9 .B796 2002
    590'.3--dc21

Printed in Malaysia
Bound in the United States of America

07 06 05 04 03 02 01    8 7 6 5 4 3 2 1

Brown Partworks
Project editor: Ben Hoare
Associate editors: Lesley Campbell-Wright, Rob Dimery, Robert Houston, Jane Lanigan, Sally McFall, Chris Marshall, Paul Thompson, Matthew D. S. Turner
Managing editor: Tim Cooke
Designer: Paul Griffin
Picture researchers: Brenda Clynch, Becky Cox
Illustrators: Ian Lycett, Catherine Ward
Indexer: Kay Ollerenshaw

Marshall Cavendish Corporation
Editorial director: Paul Bernabeo

## Authors and Consultants

Dr. Roger Avery, BSc, PhD (University of Bristol)

Rob Cave, BA (University of Plymouth)

Fergus Collins, BA (University of Liverpool)

Dr. Julia J. Day, BSc (University of Bristol), PhD (University of London)

Tom Day, BA, MA (University of Cambridge), MSc (University of Southampton)

Bridget Giles, BA (University of London)

Leon Gray, BSc (University of London)

Tim Harris, BSc (University of Reading)

Richard Hoey, BSc, MPhil (University of Manchester), MSc (University of London)

Dr. Terry J. Holt, BSc, PhD (University of Liverpool)

Dr. Robert D. Houston, BA, MA (University of Oxford), PhD (University of Bristol)

Steve Hurley, BSc (University of London), MRes (University of York)

Tom Jackson, BSc (University of Bristol)

E. Vicky Jenkins, BSc (University of Edinburgh), MSc (University of Aberdeen)

Dr. Jamie McDonald, BSc (University of York), PhD (University of Birmingham)

Dr. Robbie A. McDonald, BSc (University of St. Andrews), PhD (University of Bristol)

Dr. James W. R. Martin, BSc (University of Leeds), PhD (University of Bristol)

Dr. Tabetha Newman, BSc, PhD (University of Bristol)

Dr. J. Pimenta, BSc (University of London), PhD (University of Bristol)

Dr. Kieren Pitts, BSc, MSc (University of Exeter), PhD (University of Bristol)

Dr. Stephen J. Rossiter, BSc (University of Sussex), PhD (University of Bristol)

Dr. Sugoto Roy, PhD (University of Bristol)

Dr. Adrian Seymour, BSc, PhD (University of Bristol)

Dr. Salma H. A. Shalla, BSc, MSc, PhD (Suez Canal University, Egypt)

Dr. S. Stefanni, PhD (University of Bristol)

Steve Swaby, BA (University of Exeter)

Matthew D. S. Turner, BA (University of Loughborough), FZSL (Fellow of the Zoological Society of London)

Alastair Ward, BSc (University of Glasgow), MRes (University of York)

Dr. Michael J. Weedon, BSc, MSc, PhD (University of Bristol)

Alwyne Wheeler, former Head of the Fish Section, Natural History Museum, London

# Contents

# BARN OWL

*The bowl-shaped face of a barn owl acts like a highly efficient parabolic reflector by focusing sounds toward the owl's hidden ears.*

THERE ARE TEN SPECIES of barn owl found in various parts of the world. They differ from other owls in small details of the skeleton and in proportionately smaller eyes set in a heart-shaped facial disc. The species of barn owl familiar to most people, *Tyto alba*, has a virtually worldwide distribution and as many as 32 recognized subspecies.

The barn owl looks like a ghostly apparition when on the wing at dusk and dawn, but its body is not as white as it first appears. Only the underparts and face are pure white; the upper-parts are orange-buff, often speckled with gray and white. The barn owl has the distinction of being probably the most widespread land bird in the world. The species is found in much of the Americas, Europe, Africa, the Middle East, India, Southeast Asia and Australia, and also occurs on many oceanic islands. However, it is absent from parts of the Amazon basin, the arid Saharan region of Africa and all of northern and central Asia.

In North America, the barn owl does not breed north of Massachusetts, southern Ontario and Michigan, Iowa, Nebraska and northern California, although it is regularly recorded as a visitor farther north. Despite being fairly common in parts of its western range, the barn owl is scarce and declining in eastern North America.

## Declining populations

Changes in land use have removed many suitable nest sites and modern, intensive farming methods deprive barn owls of their prey in many areas. The species prefers to breed and roost in old buildings and hollow trees, but farmers are now less tolerant of derelict structures and rotten trees. Moreover, the barn owl preys mainly on rats, voles and mice, which have all declined as the harvesting and storage of crops becomes more efficient.

Pesticides sprayed onto agricultural land are absorbed into the bodies of the small animals that eat the crops, and these poisons gradually accumulate even further when they are eaten by predators such as owls. The result is that barn owls often become sterile. The females lay infertile eggs with thin eggshells that fail to hatch, with devastating effects on breeding success.

## Ghostly appearance

The barn owl has probably given rise to many ghost stories. It often nests and roosts in churches and empty houses and is likely to give anyone not expecting it a bad shock when its pale form flies silently past them or when they hear its eerie, drawn-out shrieks. Sometimes barn owls may be seen in broad daylight. More usually, however, they emerge at twilight. With

# BARN OWL

| | |
|---|---|
| CLASS | **Aves** |
| ORDER | **Strigiformes** |
| FAMILY | **Tytonidae** |
| GENUS AND SPECIES | ***Tyto alba*** |

ALTERNATIVE NAMES
**White owl; church owl (both archaic)**

WEIGHT
**Male: 1¼ lb. (570 g); female: 1–1½ lb.
(450–700 g)**

LENGTH
**Head to tail: 13–13¾ in. (33–35 cm);
wingspan: 33½–36½ in. (85–93 cm)**

DISTINCTIVE FEATURES
**Pure white face and underparts; orange-buff
upperparts, speckled with gray and white**

DIET
**Small mammals, birds and amphibians**

BREEDING
**Age at first breeding: 1 year; breeding
season: February–November (southern
U.S.), March–July (northern U.S.); number
of eggs: usually 4 to 7; incubation period:
30–34 days; fledging period: 50–56 days;
breeding interval: 1 or 2 broods per year**

LIFE SPAN
**Up to 15 years**

HABITAT
**Grassland, rough farmland and edges of
woods and marshes**

DISTRIBUTION
**Worldwide range includes most of the
Americas, Europe, Africa, the Middle East,
India, Southeast Asia and Australia**

STATUS
**Widespread but relatively uncommon;
scarce and declining in eastern North
America and northwestern Europe**

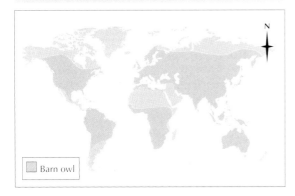

Barn owl

*Hollow trees make
ideal nest sites for
barn owls.*

their white plumage, they are easy to see, flying
about 15–20 feet (4.5–6 m) above the ground,
with fairly rapid but long wingbeats. They have
regular routes that they patrol night after night,
circling about and occasionally dropping to the
ground like a stone to catch their prey.

## Grassland hunters

Prey is taken to the nest or to a regular roost,
which is identifiable by the pellets that are
regurgitated and dropped, littering the ground
about the roost. The pellets contain a variety of
indigestible material, such as bones, fur and
insect wing cases. The barn owl's pellets are
blackish with a varnished appearance.

It is from their pellets that the diets of barn
owls and other predatory birds can be identified.
Barn owls regurgitate their pellets in set places
and the pellets accumulate, so it is possible to
obtain a very good idea of their diet by collecting
the pellets at intervals and dissecting them to
find the bones and other prey remains. A large
number of barn owl pellets were once analyzed
in Poland. The remains of nearly 16,000
vertebrates were found and identified. Of these,
95 percent were small mammals, 4 percent birds
and the remainder, amphibians.

In the United States, the staple prey items of
the barn owl are mice, moles, shrews and cotton
rats. Occasionally jack rabbits, bats, musk rats
and skunks are taken. Birds represent a smaller
part of the owl's diet: pigeons, jays, rails, flickers,

white eggs are laid, but there may be as few as three or as many as 11. They are incubated for nearly 5 weeks by the female alone, which remains on the nest, being fed by the male.

The young hatch out at different times because the female begins incubating the first egg as soon as it is laid, so each egg begins its development before the next is laid. In many birds incubation does not begin until all the eggs have been laid, so they all hatch at once. It has been suggested that the staggered hatching of barn owls' eggs helps to reduce the strain of providing enough food for them, because they will not all be requiring large quantities of food at once. The chicks leave the nest after 7–8 weeks to find territories of their own, where they stay for the rest of their lives.

## Dead-shot in the dark

At one time it was thought that barn owls hunted by sight. Certainly they have very keen sight, perhaps a hundred times as keen as that of humans, but experiments have shown that the owls can catch their prey in total darkness, where it is absolutely impossible to see anything.

In one experiment a tame barn owl was placed in a pitch-black room and a mouse was allowed to scuffle through leaf litter on the floor. After a short pause the owl would swoop at the ground and when the lights were put on it was back on its perch with the mouse. The experiment was repeated no less than 17 times, and the owl only missed four times. To demonstrate that the owl was not responding to the smell or heat emitted by the mice, wads of paper were drawn across the floor, and these too were captured without difficulty.

A detailed examination of a barn owl's ears shows them to be very well developed, and there are flaps of skin forming "outer ears" hidden under the feathers. These flaps are not placed symmetrically about the head, which means that sound coming to one ear follows a slightly different path from that going to the other ear. Thus a sound is picked up by one ear slightly before or after the other. It is this fractional difference in timing that enables an owl to judge the position of its prey.

To make life even more hazardous for a small animal, the long flight feathers of a barn owl's wings are tipped with down on the leading, trailing and upper surfaces. This deadens the noise of the owl's wingbeats so the intended prey has no warning of attack, unless it, too, has especially sensitive ears. Such animals include the kangaroo rats of the genus *Dipodomys*, which have ears sensitive enough to hear even the very faint sounds a barn owl makes as it is about to strike.

*Barn owls have modified wing feathers that deaden the sound of their approach.*

green herons and bluebirds have all been recorded as barn owl prey. The barn owl itself sometimes falls prey to the much larger great horned owl, *Bubo virginianus*, and very rarely to the prairie falcon, *Falco mexicanus*.

The large number of small mammals included in the barn owl's diet shows the useful role played by the species because its regular prey feeds on crops. The numbers that a barn owl can catch are shown by observations made of a single owl. In only 20 minutes it had caught 16 mice, 3 gophers, 1 rat and 1 squirrel. The haul gives an indication of the impact that barn owls have on small mammal populations.

## Staggered breeding

At the start of the breeding season, piles of prey can be found at a barn owl's nest site. This is a sign that a pair is about to breed, for the male collects extra food to feed to the female. There is no nest made, the eggs are merely laid on an accumulation of pellets. Usually four to seven

# BARN SWALLOW

## Swallows and martins

Barn swallows are known simply as "swallows" in Britain, where they are the only breeding species of swallow. However, the family to which they belong, Hirundinidae, contains no less than 73 other species spread throughout 16 to 19 genera; the exact number depending on which classification system is used. This large family of birds includes both the swallows and the martins, the differences between which are not easy to define. Indeed, one species, *Riparia riparia*, is confusingly known as the bank swallow in the United States and as the sand martin in Britain. For this reason, many ornithologists tend to use the term "hirundine" to refer to any member of the Hirundinidae family. A large flock of "hirundines" catching insects over a lake or freshly mown field could therefore include several species of martin as well as various swallow species.

The greatest concentration of swallow and martin species is to be found in Africa. Some are found there all year, while several Eurasian species, including the barn swallow,

*Barn swallows are extremely agile fliers, catching all of their insect prey in midair.*

Oᴺᴇ ᴏꜰ ᴛʜᴇ ʙᴇꜱᴛ-ʟᴏᴠᴇᴅ and most studied birds in the world, the barn swallow also has the widest distribution of any swallow. In spring and summer this species breeds right across North America, Europe and Asia. In fact, the barn swallow's huge breeding range includes virtually all land lying north of the Tropic of Cancer, apart from the northernmost latitudes: Alaska and northern Canada, Scandinavia and Siberia. Before the onset of winter, when the barn swallow's prey of flying insects becomes scarce, all of the Northern Hemisphere populations migrate southward, to tropical South America, Africa, India and Southeast Asia.

Barn swallows have glossy, blue-black upperparts, which contrast strongly with paler underparts that vary in tone according to the subspecies. For example, North American birds have rather warm, orange-buff undersides, while those of European birds are white and Egyptian birds are bright chestnut. All subspecies of the barn swallow also have a red patch on the face and throat, below which lies a blue collar. Juvenile birds are much duller than adults, their plumage tending to be brownish.

migrate there to avoid the northern winter. Nine species of swallow and martin breed in the United States. These include the cliff swallow, *Hirundo pyrrhonota*, and the tree swallow, *Tachycineta bicolor*, both of which breed throughout North America and winter as far south as northern Argentina. Another familiar North American species is the purple martin, *Progne subis*, which is common in town gardens. Nearly all purple martins now nest in artificial martin houses provided by humans. Originally, the purple martin nested in natural tree holes and caves and on cliff crevices.

Among the remaining species of hirundine is the red-rumped swallow, *H. daurica*, which is found mainly in dry, hilly country in southern Europe and Asia and parts of Africa. It has several close relatives that are a familiar sight in Africa, including the rufous-chested swallow, *H. semirufa*, and the mosque swallow, *H. senegalensis*. Not all hirundines are common and frequently seen, however. A few have very restricted ranges. An example is the golden swallow, *T. euchrysea*, native to the Caribbean islands of Jamaica and Hispaniola.

*Barn swallows spend most of their waking hours on the wing, visiting the ground only to collect mud for their cup-shaped nests.*

## BARN SWALLOW

| | |
|---|---|
| CLASS | **Aves** |
| ORDER | **Passeriformes** |
| FAMILY | **Hirundinidae** |
| GENUS AND SPECIES | *Hirundo rustica* |

ALTERNATIVE NAMES
**Swallow; chimney swallow; house swallow**

WEIGHT
**½–¾ oz. (14–21g)**

LENGTH
**Head to tail: 6½–7½ in. (17–19 cm); wingspan: 12½–13¾ in. (32–35 cm)**

DISTINCTIVE FEATURES
**Slender body; small bill with wide gape; long, forked tail with two long streamers; glossy blue above and buff, chestnut or white below; red patch on face and throat**

DIET
**Flying insects, especially flies and aphids**

BREEDING
**Age at first breeding: 1 year; breeding season: March–July, varies across range; number of eggs: typically 4 or 5; incubation period: 11–19 days; fledging period: 18–23 days; breeding interval: 2 broods per year**

LIFE SPAN
**Up to 16 years; usually less than 4 years**

HABITAT
**All kinds of open country, especially near water. Avoids dense woodland, mountains, deserts and city centers.**

DISTRIBUTION
**Breeds worldwide north of Tropic of Cancer; winters in South America, sub-Saharan Africa, India and Southeast Asia**

STATUS
**Common and often abundant, but many populations in western Europe decreasing**

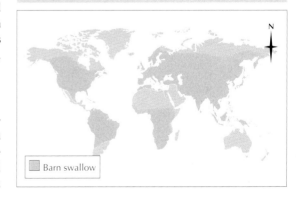

Barn swallow

## Life on the wing

Regardless of their common names, swallows and martins share a number of instantly recognizable characteristics. They have very slender, streamlined bodies with long, pointed wings. All have extremely short, compressed bills that open wide to reveal a proportionately huge gape. They feed by catching flying insects in midflight, trawling through the air with their bills held wide open to serve as nets. To help them catch their prey the birds are all superb, graceful fliers, able to maneuver with great precision.

Barn swallows spend much of their day on the wing, perching occasionally on prominent twigs and reeds, and especially on telephone wires. They even drink while airborne, by swooping low over the surface of rivers and lakes to scoop water in their bills, without stopping. Barn swallows come to the ground only to collect mud for building a nest. Like other swallows, they shuffle awkwardly because their feet and legs are small compared with the rest of the body, but this not does matter as they are adapted for a largely aerial existence.

The song of barn swallows is a musical twitter, delivered in midair. It is normally heard when the swallows fly together in parties. An exception is when hundreds of barn swallows roost together in trees and reed beds in the fall, before setting off on their southbound migration.

## Long-haul migrants

To many people living in the Northern Hemisphere, the appearance of barn swallows in spring is a welcome sight. The birds are sometimes even regarded as the bringers of good fortune. The timing of their northerly migration in spring depends upon the prevailing weather both in the wintering grounds at the time of departure and while en route. As a result the arrival dates of barn swallows in their breeding grounds may vary by 2 weeks or more from one year to another. In addition, there are individuals that arrive ahead of the main stream and there are those that remain after the rest have gone south again in the fall.

A small number of barn swallows, belonging to southern populations from regions such as Texas, Florida and Spain, do not migrate at all. The result is that in the United States and comparable latitudes barn swallows are recorded in every month of the year. Nevertheless, the vast majority of barn swallows make an annual round-trip of thousands of miles to guarantee a healthy supply of flying insect prey.

## Association with humans

There is a tendency for numerous pairs of barn swallows to nest fairly close together. Up to 30 pairs breed in these loose colonies. Since the swallows' feeding space—the air—is abundantly supplied with food, a territorial instinct is of limited use. The nest is typically a shallow cup made of pellets of mud, reinforced with pieces of dry grass. Originally the nests were built on cliff ledges and on the branches of trees, but today most are located on buildings and other artificial structures. Popular nest sites include beams and under eaves, while unusual sites include farm machinery, lamp shades and picture frames. The fidelity of barn swallows to a spot in a particular building has been observed many times. A pair of swallows might have its nest in a barn or outhouse, reached by flying through an open window or door. Coming to the same place a year later the swallows find the window or door is shut, and linger in a distressed state.

Female barn swallows lay clutches of up to seven white eggs and incubate them for about 2–3 weeks. The young stay in the nest for about 3 weeks and are fed by both parents. There may be two broods a year, except at the latitudinal limit of the breeding range. The juveniles from an early brood sometimes help feed the young of the next, to which they are related.

In its European breeding range the barn swallow is faced with a serious shortage of nest-sites and food. A nesting swallow needs mud to make its nest, some irregularity in a building upon which to build it and plentiful small flying insects for food. However, modern farm buildings provide fewer beams, rafters and other convenient nesting sites, while the use of powerful insecticides has greatly reduced the populations of insects on which swallows feed.

*In North America and Europe most barn swallows nest on buildings. Pairs often return to the same nesting site year after year.*

# BARRACUDA

*The great barracuda is by far the largest and most formidable species of barracuda, but its massive jaws and powerful, torpedo-shaped body are typical of the whole family.*

THESE HIGHLY AGGRESSIVE predators have a powerful, long-bodied form, with a jutting lower jaw and a wicked-looking set of long teeth. Fishermen, in handling even the dead fish, treat them with respect. There are more than 20 species of barracuda, but their well known reputation for launching unprovoked attacks is not entirely justified and most species are in truth harmless to humans. Nevertheless, there are several authentic records of barracuda attacks, most of which involve the great barracuda, the giant of the family.

Great barracuda may reach a length of over 6 feet (1.8 m) and are found in most of the world's tropical seas. The northern barracuda, of the western North Atlantic, reaches only 18 inches (46 cm), whereas the European barracuda, of the Mediterranean and eastern Atlantic, can grow to 36 inches (92 cm).

## Voracious hunters

More fearful to some people than even sharks, the larger species of barracuda are among the most voracious of all predatory fish. Barracuda swim fast and hunt a wide range of other fish, especially plankton-feeding species. They charge straight through the shoals they have targeted, attacking with snapping bites. Barracuda have superb maneuverability, suddenly changing direction to catch their prey.

Small and half-grown barracuda swim together in shoals, whereas the larger individuals tend to be solitary. A lone barracuda attacks swiftly, bites cleanly and does not repeat its attack; shoaling barracuda seldom attack humans. Legend used to state that when a shoal of barracuda has eaten enough, it herds all the surviving prey fish into shallow water and keeps guard until ready for another meal.

Barracuda hunt by sight rather than smell, as sharks do, and safety advice given to bathers and divers reflects this fact. For example, murky water should be avoided if possible because a barracuda, aware of every movement due to its keen eyesight, may overestimate a swimmer's size, thereby exaggerating the danger he or she represents, and launch an attack. A metallic object flashing in clear water looks just like a fish to a barracuda and can stimulate the attack response. It is also not unknown for a barracuda to snatch a captured fish from the belt of a passing skin-diver.

# BARRACUDA

| | |
|---|---|
| CLASS | **Actinopterygii** |
| ORDER | **Perciformes** |
| FAMILY | **Sphyraenidae** |
| GENUS | ***Sphyraena*** |
| SPECIES | **20, including great barracuda, *S. barracuda*; California barracuda, *S. argentea*; guaguanche, *S. guachancho*; northern barracuda, *S. borealis*; European barracuda, *S. sphyraena*** |

ALTERNATIVE NAMES
**Great barracuda: picuda, becuna; California barracuda: Pacific barracuda**

WEIGHT
**Up to 88 lb. (40 kg)**

LENGTH
**Up to 6 ft. (1.8 m); most species usually 2–4 ft. (0.6–1.2 m)**

DISTINCTIVE FEATURES
**Long, slender body; large, snoutlike mouth with jutting lower jaw; long teeth**

DIET
**Wide variety of fish, especially shoaling, plankton-eating species**

BREEDING
**Poorly known**

LIFE SPAN
**Up to 10 years**

HABITAT
**Wide range of marine habitats, especially shallow, coastal waters and coral reefs. Young occasionally enter estuaries and mangrove swamps.**

DISTRIBUTION
**Worldwide in tropical, subtropical and warm temperate waters**

STATUS
**Common**

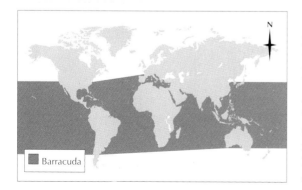

Barracuda

## Barracuda research

Virtually all of the interest in barracuda has been concentrated on their behavior toward humans and on their use for food. On two occasions American scientists have collected reports of alleged attacks on humans. These amount to fewer than 40 in total, which makes barracuda less dangerous in aggregate than sharks. To a large extent the notoriety of barracuda is the result of what appears to be no more than insatiable curiosity. They will trail a scubadiver, watching his or her movements and generating an uncomfortable feeling. Even so, there are records of a person standing in no more than 1 foot (30 cm) of water having the flesh bitten from the lower leg, or the bone almost severed.

The life history and breeding behavior of barracuda are relatively little known. Barracuda spawn communally in deep water offshore. There is no parental care, and ocean currents distribute the larvae and young.

## Poisonous flesh

All barracuda are regarded as good food fish, although there is some prejudice against them because their flesh is, on occasion, highly poisonous. This may be a seasonal danger, the flesh being poisonous at some times of the year and not at others, but it is also due to a condition known as ciguatera. Toxins, originating in toxic diatoms (unicellular algae), accumulate in the bodies of plant-eating fish species. The toxins accumulate further in the predators of these vegetarian fish, and become ever more concentrated higher up the food chain. Thus the flesh of certain barracuda often contains high levels of the toxins, which cause sickness, and even death, in humans that eat the fish.

*Barracuda are often inquisitive and shoals will allow a close approach. This large shoal of young fish was photographed off the coast of Borneo in Southeast Asia.*

# BASILISK

*Basilisks are among the handful of reptiles and amphibians that have evolved the ability to sprint across water as a means of escaping predators.*

THE FOUR SPECIES of basilisk, all of which live in tropical America, share an unusual appearance and peculiar habits. The common basilisk, *Basiliscus basiliscus*, is typical. The male grows to 24 inches (61 cm) in length, including a long, tapering tail, and has a striking crest of skin on the head reminiscent of a cock's comb. The crest continues down the midline of the back and on to the first half of the tail. Females are slightly smaller than males and lack the crest, which is also absent in juveniles.

Another outstanding feature of basilisks is their long hind legs, which end in long toes fringed with scales. The hind limbs bear some similarity to those of frogs and, although not webbed, the feet are also froglike in that they have a large sole. The front legs of basilisks are relatively small by comparison.

## Running on water

In South America basilisks are known by the names of *Jesus Cristo* lizard and *paso-rios*, or river-crosser, because of their remarkable ability to run on water. They live among thick shrubs and trees bordering rivers and streams, into which they drop the moment they are disturbed. The lizards either move straight to the bottom of the water and stay there for a while, surfacing when the intruder has had time to move away, or else race over the water's surface with their body semi-erect.

Basilisks also run over the ground and along branches of trees in much the same way, with their long tails held out behind and curving slightly upward for balance. Their hind legs take large strides recalling those of running ostriches and emus. A few other lizards can sprint on land like this, but it seems that they must first gather speed by running on all-fours, later lifting the front part of the body and the forelegs from the ground. Basilisks, on the other hand, seem to be able to adopt the semi-erect position from a standing start.

## How do they do it?

The usual explanation of basilisks' ability to run over water is that they travel so fast they do not have time to sink. It is certainly true that, provided basilisks move quickly, the soles of their feet do not break through the surface film. As their pace slackens, the lizards drop on to all-fours, becoming partially submerged. They finish the journey by swimming.

The lightweight bodies of basilisks, combined with their long tails and the considerable spread of their long-fringed toes, are important

# BASILISKS

| | |
|---|---|
| CLASS | **Reptilia** |
| ORDER | **Squamata** |
| FAMILY | **Iguanidae** |
| GENUS | ***Basiliscus*** |
| SPECIES | **4, including common basilisk, *B. basiliscus*; and plumed basilisk, *B. plumifrons*** |

ALTERNATIVE NAMES
**Common basilisk: Jesus lizard; plumed basilisk: leafy plumb-tree basilisk**

LENGTH
**Up to 31½ in. (80 cm) including tail**

DISTINCTIVE FEATURES
**Sail-like crest on head and along top of back and tail (male only); long, froglike hind legs with long toes; usually green or brown**

DIET
**Mainly insects and fruits**

BREEDING
**Breeding season: May–June; number of eggs: up to 12; hatching period: about 90 days**

LIFE SPAN
**Probably 10–15 years**

HABITAT
**Thick vegetation near to rivers and streams**

DISTRIBUTION
**Mexico south to Venezuela, Colombia and Ecuador**

STATUS
**Locally common**

☐ Basilisks

*When in full flight basilisks adopt a semi-erect posture and take great strides with their hind legs.*

in this act of scuttering across water. At least one species of frog uses a similar means of escape, although its progress more closely resembles the flight action of a flat pebble over water.

Recent research has demonstrated how a running basilisk can generate enough upward force to stay above water. Each of its feet flares outwards upon impact with the water, trapping a pocket of air beneath the sole. As the air pocket is forced through the water, it creates lift.

It is interesting to note that the unrelated sail-fin lizard, *Hydrosaurus pustulatus*, has developed habits similar to those of basilisks, including the feat of running on water. The sail-fin lizard is native to the Philippines and is a member of the family Agamidae, whereas basilisks belong to the family Iguanidae. These geographically distant lizards have undergone evolutionary change in similar but entirely separate environments, producing similarly designed animals to fit vacant niches. This phenomenon is known as convergent evolution.

## Breeding
Basilisks breed in May and June. The female common basilisk digs a cavity 3 inches (7.5 cm) deep in the soil at the base of a tree. Having done this she stations herself with her cloaca over the hole and lays up to 12 eggs, covering the clutch with soil. The hatching period depends on the temperature and species, but is usually about 90 days. The young basilisks inside cut criss-cross slits in their parchment-like shells, using an egg tooth on the snout. They take 30–40 minutes to climb out of the shells, and when newly hatched are about 3 inches (7.5 cm) long.

## Medieval myth
Basilisks are named after a mythological creature that was said to kill any living thing with its glance. However, there is nothing dangerous about the fictional monster's namesake. The original basilisk was reputedly the king of serpents and according to ancient chroniclers was hatched from an egg laid by an elderly cockerel, which was then incubated by a toad.

# BASKET STAR

**Basket stars cling to a variety of stationary or slow-moving animals, including soft coral (above) and shells.**

fully spread arms. In these specimens the disc, as the central body is called, can attain a diameter of about 4 inches (10 cm). In other types of echinoderm, such as starfish and sea urchins, the entire surface of the body is covered with calcareous knobs, tubercles, plates or spines. Basket stars, however, are instead covered with a skin in which chalky granules, and sometimes small tubercles, are embedded.

Living basket stars usually have a delicate coloration. Those belonging to the best known genus, *Gorgonocephalus*, are white, tinged with salmon pink on the radial ridges of the disc, with dull blue between the ridges. The arms are also pinkish. Other basket stars are various subtle shades of pale yellow, orange, pink and brown.

Basket stars are far less mobile than starfish and brittle stars. They cling to sedentary marine animals living on the seabed, especially shells and the treelike soft corals. Alternatively, they cling to solid objects, such as boulders, stones, ship anchors and shipwrecks. While feeding, basket stars hold on to their host or support with two arms and spread the remaining three to catch passing food particles. They do change position regularly, but move with a rowing motion of the arms rather than by crawling.

Basket stars are echinoderms and are closely related to brittle stars and starfish. Most species are characterized by the copious branching of their five arms. In these species, the typical basket stars, each arm forks near its base and each arm of the fork divides in two, until the five arms come to resemble a form of basketwork. The arms of dead specimens curl on themselves so that the delicate outer branches form a tangled mass reminiscent of the fabled Gorgon's head. In Greek mythology the Gorgons were three sisters who had snakes instead of hair on their heads, and whose very glance turned people to stone.

In certain species of basket star the arms are not branched, but rather long and tendril-like. However, in all basket stars the arm joints are articulated, with the result that they can be coiled vertically, whereas brittle stars can manage only a lateral curvature.

## Sedentary lifestyle
Basket stars live throughout the world's seas at depths of up to 6,600 feet (2,000 m). The largest can measure as much as 2 feet (0.6 m) across the

## Varied feeding strategies
On rocky seabeds basket stars tend to be gregarious, although their feeding habits vary with both age and, to some extent, the species. Generally, young basket stars are particulate feeders: they feed on organic detritus, that is minute particles created by the decay and break-up of plant and animal bodies. There is a continuous "rain" of such material from the upper layers of the ocean, which are rich in life, down to the depths where basket stars live. The skin on the arms of basket stars secretes mucus, to which any floating organic material adheres. Young basket stars simply extend their branched arms to their full extent and catch the floating particles, which are rolled into a clump and then passed along to the mouth.

Adult basket stars are predatory as well as being scavengers, and have a more active method of feeding. When an adult is stimulated by a small animal touching one of its arms, it

## BASKET STARS

| | |
|---|---|
| PHYLUM | **Echinodermata** |
| CLASS | **Ophiuroidea** |
| ORDER | **Euryaleae** |
| FAMILY | **Euryalidae** |
| GENUS | ***Gorgonocephalus, Astrophytum, Ophiocoma, Ophiothrix*; others** |
| SPECIES | **There are about 2,000 species of basket stars and brittle stars** |

ALTERNATIVE NAME
**Gorgon's head**

LENGTH
**Central disc: up to 4 in. (10 cm); arm spread: up to 24 in. (60 cm)**

DISTINCTIVE FEATURES
**Five branched arms, often ending in fine tendrils; more flexible than closely related brittle stars**

DIET
**Tiny organic particles, zooplankton and small crustaceans**

BREEDING
**Poorly known; sexes are separate**

LIFE SPAN
**Not known**

HABITAT
**Seabed at 65–6,600 ft. (20–2,000 m). Cling to solid objects and sedentary animals.**

DISTRIBUTION
**Worldwide, including Arctic and Antarctic**

STATUS
**Superabundant**

stretches its arms sideways and upward in such a way that they create a bowl-shaped openwork basket. If a small swimming animal, such as a copepod, touches any part of the basket star, that part coils quickly round it. The arm's other branches help out with larger prey, such as small shrimps, gradually engulfing the victims. When several prey items have been seized the whole arm bends inward to pass the food to the basket star's waiting mouth.

Predatory feeding by adult basket stars takes place mainly at night. They emerge from their hiding places at nightfall, orientating themselves in such a way that that their open arms face the prevailing current. Researchers have found that at least one species of basket star moves with the tides, changing position so that it faces first the incoming current and then the outgoing current. There is also some evidence to suggest that nocturnal basket stars do not begin digesting captured prey until dawn. The largest species can tackle shrimps and other crustaceans up to a size of 1¼ inches (3 cm).

*Each arm of a basket star branches many times to form an intricate basketwork perfectly adapted for trapping drifting food particles.*

### Mysterious scavengers

Very little is known concerning the reproduction and development of basket stars. The sexes are separate and in many species the females brood their young underneath their bodies until the offspring are quite large. The young of one species of basket star live parasitically on a particular soft coral, Alcyonacean. When the juveniles of this species are old enough for the arms to start branching, they leave the coral and wander until they locate—and can therefore cling to—an adult of their own species.

Basket stars are among the most bizarre of all marine animals. Occasionally one is cast ashore following a storm, or is brought to the surface on an anchor chain that has been left undisturbed for some time. The fact that serious scientists should see in basket stars a resemblance to the mythical Gorgons is sufficient indication of the strangeness of their appearance. It is, indeed, not beyond the bounds of possibility that a basket star that had been washed up on the Greek coast may have given rise to the myth of the Gorgons. Such an animal must have fascinated anyone finding it for the first time.

# BASKING SHARK

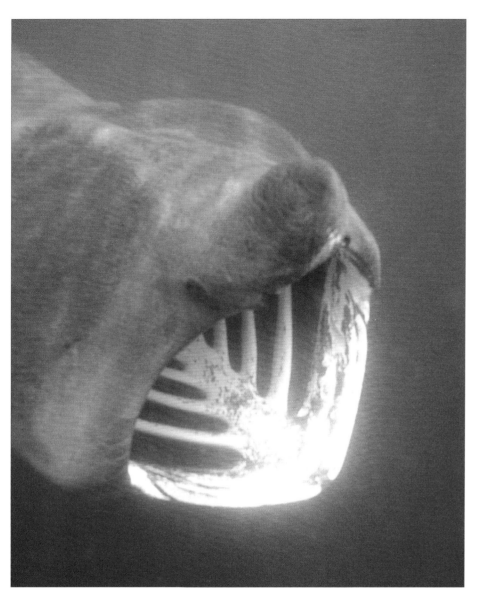

The basking shark may look formidable, but is neither aggressive nor carnivorous. Deposits of plankton, the main food, are visible inside this shark's mouth.

## Filter-feeding giant

The basking shark's body varies from bluish-gray to grayish-brown and, sometimes, almost black. Its underparts are always whitish. The shark has minute teeth adapted to its plankton diet, very large gill slits that almost encircle the body behind the head, and curious rakers on its hooplike gill arches, which filter plankton from the water.

On a number of occasions in the past the decomposing body of a basking shark has been washed ashore and has been mistaken for the carcass of a monstrous sea serpent. In such instances the basking shark's gill-rakers, exposed by the process of decomposition, appear to have been interpreted by the onlookers as the sea serpent's mane.

## Ocean cruisers

With its huge mouth open like a dragnet, the basking shark swims through the sea, large quantities of water entering its mouth and passing across the gills. The gill-rakers sieve minute plankton from the water, which are swallowed. In a sense the basking shark is "vacuuming" the sea. It has been estimated that a shark can process roughly 1,800 gallons (6,815 l) of water per hour.

The basking shark is a relatively sluggish swimmer. It enters coastal waters in summer, singly, in twos or threes, or more rarely in shoals of 60 or more. The largest sighting of basking sharks occurred in the spring of 1998 when a shoal of 500 was sighted off the Lizard Peninsula in Cornwall, southwestern England. During good weather, a basking shark cruises slowly, or basks, at the surface, with its prominent dorsal fin, and sometimes the upper lobe of its tail fin, showing above the water. Favored feeding grounds are the plankton-rich fronts that occur between warm, turbid (cloudy) coastal waters and cooler, clearer oceanic waters.

Not until the early 1950s were clues obtained as to what happened to basking sharks in winter. Several caught in the North Sea in early winter were found to lack gill rakers, which are essential for feeding, and it became clear that basking sharks shed their gill-rakers and cease to feed at this time. During the fall the amount of plankton decreases. Therefore basking sharks stop feeding and probably retire to deeper waters. They may

ONE OF THE LARGEST SHARKS, the basking shark can reach just over 49 feet (15 m) in length. It is a harmless, plankton-eating fish of cool and temperate seas throughout the world, with the largest numbers present in the North Atlantic. Only the whale shark, *Rhincodon typus*, is bigger than the basking shark. But in spite of its large size (its nearest relative is the great white shark) and the frequency with which it is seen, there are still many serious gaps in scientific knowledge of the basking shark's habits.

The lack of detailed information about the basking shark is even more surprising considering that it has been caught commercially in its tens of thousands for many years. Today, smaller numbers are still killed annually, although the species enjoys full legal protection in many areas of the world.

# BASKING SHARK

| | |
|---|---|
| CLASS | **Chondrichthyes** |
| ORDER | **Lamniformes** |
| FAMILY | **Cetorhinidae** |
| GENUS AND SPECIES | ***Cetorhinus maximus*** |

WEIGHT
**About 8820 lb. (4,000 kg) in typical sharks of 32¾ ft (10 m) in length**

LENGTH
**Up to 49 ft. (15 m), usually less**

DISTINCTIVE FEATURES
**Very large size; huge mouth with large gill-rakers; highly elongated gill slits; tall, triangular dorsal fin**

DIET
**Plankton, including both invertebrates and small vertebrates**

BREEDING
**Poorly known**

LIFE SPAN
**Likely to be tens of years**

HABITAT
**Plankton-rich seas; deeper waters in winter**

DISTRIBUTION
**Cool and temperate waters worldwide; absent from western Pacific, northern and western Indian Ocean, North Sea and parts of Atlantic (especially in east)**

STATUS
**Vulnerable; little population data available**

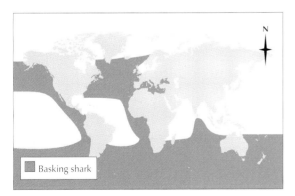

Basking shark

that this exercise is intended to remove parasites, such as groups of lampreys, which attach themselves to the sharks' skin.

## Low-energy diet

The plankton consumed by basking sharks is largely composed of minute, shrimplike copepods (a type of crustacean), the eggs of other fish and arrow-worms. In spring and summer these foods are abundant, but even so the sharks have to put considerable effort into searching out food sources for themselves.

A shark needs the equivalent of ⅓ horsepower to swim. This means taking in 663 calories every hour merely to replace the energy used in swimming to collect the food. It has been estimated than an average-sized basking shark would filter about 2½ pounds (1.1 kg) of plankton an hour under the most favorable conditions for November, when plankton supply has fallen for the winter. This would yield only 410 calories an hour. In November a basking shark would therefore be using up markedly more energy in feeding than it would be obtaining from its food. These figures were obtained using a variety of methods. These included measuring the size of a basking shark's mouth, calculating the flow of water through it at a constant 2 knots (3.5 km/h), and measuring the amount of plankton in a known quantity of seawater.

## Mysterious life history

Virtually nothing is known about breeding in basking sharks. It has always been assumed that the young are born alive, simply because this is the case with many other sharks. If, however, basking sharks lay eggs, they would most likely be contained within a leathery capsule. When the female of an egg-laying species of shark is cut open, unlaid eggs are often found in the oviducts.

*In the spring and summer basking sharks congregate in cloudy, plankton-rich waters.*

even hibernate. However, although the basking sharks' summer haunts are well-known, their winter waters remain something of a mystery.

Basking sharks are sometimes observed leaping out of the sea, half-somersaulting and then belly-flopping back into the water, in an impressive display known as breaching. It is believed

Yet no egg-capsules have been found in any female basking shark captured, and none have ever been found in the sea. In 1923, however, off the coast of Norway, a female basking shark, at the moment of capture, gave birth to six young. Five of these escaped and swam away. The sixth was dead. It was 5 feet (1.5 m) long and weighed 18 pounds (8.2 kg). These are still the only young basking sharks ever to have been seen.

Basking sharks are hard to capture except by those who are experienced in the fishing industry. Most of our knowledge of the species' habits is thus derived from indirect studies. Similar detective work has been used with regards to the life history of this mysterious creature. It has been found that the backbones, or vertebrae, of basking sharks have growth-rings similar to those in a tree-trunk. Using these, it has been shown that most basking sharks examined by scientists fall into two distinct age groups: 5–6 years and 8–9 years.

The probability is that basking sharks do not visit inshore waters, where they can be caught, until they are sexually mature, at 3–5 years of age. Having mated, the sharks disappear for 2 years, perhaps returning to deep waters. During this time they are likely to produce their young. The young basking sharks remain in deep water for the next 3–5 years, while the parents again enter inshore waters, being now 8–9 years old.

Basking sharks are currently the subject of intense study, including the use of satellite tracking. They have also become a summer tourist attraction in parts of the United Kingdom, such as the Isle of Man, the Irish Sea and Cornwall, at the southwestern tip of England. This increased scrutiny may finally solve some of the riddles surrounding these leviathans.

## A threatened species

Between 1989 and 1996 the frequency of basking shark sightings decreased by 85 percent and there is now great concern for the species' survival. In response to this dilemma, the charity Worldwide Fund for Nature has set up a group to monitor the numbers of basking sharks over a period of 3 years. In the past the basking shark was usually caught for its liver. The shark's liver is large and may represent up to 25 percent of the overall body weight of the fish. It was used to provide liver oil, specialist aviation oils and cosmetics. However, today it is the rising demand for shark's fin soup in East Asia that is posing a real threat to the survival of the basking shark. This Chinese delicacy uses the shark's dorsal fin as its main ingredient, and a single ton of dorsal fins can fetch as much as $32,000. The basking shark's slow reproductive rate makes it highly vulnerable to commercial exploitation. It breeds infrequently, and its young mature slowly.

*The basking shark's huge gill slits almost completely encircle its body. The gills are used for breathing, as in all fish, but also have rakers that filter plankton from the water.*

# BASS

THE MANY SPECIES of fish commonly known as bass are members of two entirely unrelated families, which has frequently given rise to confusion. One of these groups contains freshwater fish native to North American lakes and rivers. This family is the sunfish, or Centrarchidae, and it includes species such as the largemouth bass and the smallmouth bass. The other group consists mainly of marine fish found throughout the world's tropical and temperate waters, but it also includes a few freshwater species. This family is the sea bass, or Serranidae. Among its members are the common bass of the eastern North Atlantic, Mediterranean and Black Sea, and the giant sea bass, which is found on the western coastline of North and Central America.

Although unrelated, the fish in these two families share a number of characteristics. They are generally large and of athletic build, with prominent, spiny fins. All are voracious predators, hunting a wide range of smaller fish, as well as crustaceans and other aquatic animals. Several species of bass are important sport fish because they have delicious flesh and are strong, putting up a determined fight against anglers. However, overfishing is a growing problem and fishing quotas are enforced for some species.

## Common bass

The common, or European, bass is at the root of all the confusion surrounding the names of these various fish. The name bass was originally taken overseas by emigrants from Britain, with the result that it has been applied, with or without some qualifying word, to a number of spiny-finned fish that live in a variety of both marine and freshwater habitats.

The fins of the common bass are so spiny that some of them can pierce human flesh, and the species also has spines on the gill-covers. Its large mouth is equally well armed. Besides the usual teeth in the jaws, the common bass has teeth on every surface of the mouth, including even the tongue. It is uniformly silver gray, with a slight tinge of pink at the bases of the fins. The common bass bears a superficial likeness to the Atlantic salmon, *Salmo salar*, and like that species its flesh is slightly pink.

Common bass feed largely on smaller fish, especially sardines, sprats and sand eels, and

supplement this diet with crustaceans, including prawns, shrimps and crabs. They move inshore in June and remain there until October, when they return out to sea. In the summer common bass may enter estuaries, particularly on the southern and western coasts of Britain, where they are caught by a bait towed behind a boat or by casting from the beach.

Spawning takes place either at sea or in brackish (slightly salty) water in estuaries, from May to the end of August. In the sea the eggs are just buoyant enough to float, whereas in fresh water they sink. They hatch in 6 days. The young fish, known as fry, grow rapidly, and by the fall are 4–6 inches (10.2–15.2 cm) long. They follow the adults in their migration out to sea.

## Other species of sea bass

The giant sea bass frequents the shore, and is extremely popular with the anglers of the West Coast. It is a ruthless predator and can grow to a huge size. Another species of sea bass, the stone bass, is widely distributed in the Atlantic and Mediterranean. It has a habit of swimming beside any wreckage and among floating logs, planks and boxes, and also frequents wrecks lying on the seabed. Also known as the wreckfish, it regularly reaches weights of 100 pounds (45 kg). It is highly aggressive, often attacking and killing fish larger than itself.

*Sea bass gather in large shoals off the western seaboard of North America and are one of the main targets of sport fishers.*

163

*A formidable hunter, the largemouth bass lies unseen in wait for passing prey.*

## BASS

| | |
|---|---|
| CLASS | **Osteichthyes** |
| ORDER | **Perciformes** |

FAMILY (1) **Sea bass, Serranidae**

GENUS **Several, including *Morone, Stereolepis* and *Polyprion***

SPECIES **Common bass, *M. labrax*; giant sea bass, *S. gigas*; others**

FAMILY (2) **Sunfish, Centrarchidae**

GENUS **Several, including *Micropterus***

SPECIES **Largemouth bass, *M. salmoides*; smallmouth bass, *M. dolomieui*; others**

WEIGHT
**Sea bass: up to 880 lb. (400 kg). Sunfish: up to 22 lb. (10 kg).**

LENGTH
**Sea bass: up to 9¾ ft. (3 m). Sunfish: up to 31½ in. (80 cm).**

DISTINCTIVE FEATURES
**Robust body; prominent, spiny fins**

DIET
**Sea bass: fish and crustaceans. Sunfish: fish, amphibians and aquatic invertebrates.**

BREEDING
**Varies according to species**

LIFE SPAN
**Usually up to 10 years**

HABITAT
**Sea bass: marine habitats, some species in fresh water. Sunfish: lakes and rivers.**

DISTRIBUTION
**Sea bass: worldwide. Sunfish: North America.**

STATUS
**Common; often locally abundant**

## Largemouth bass

The best-known member of the North American sunfish family is the largemouth bass. As its name suggests, it differs from its close relative the smallmouth bass in having a larger mouth and body size. Its powerful jaws reach further back than the level of the eyes. The largemouth bass has the belligerence of the marine wreckfish, hunting a wide range of fish, tadpoles, worms, snails, crayfish and amphibians. Largemouth bass are also cannibalistic, often taking smaller individuals of their own species.

Unlike sea bass, the largemouth bass and its relatives in the sunfish family tend to build nests for their eggs. Breeding takes place in summer, when the male digs a shallow scrape in the bed of the lake or river. After spawning, the female leaves the male to guard the eggs. Once the eggs have hatched, he continues to guard the young fish, and will readily attack intruders in defense of the offspring. At first the fry feed on insect larvae and other small prey, but as they increase in size the young bass hunt a wider range of prey. The rate at which they grow is dependent on a variety of factors, including water temperature, but they typically reach sexual maturity within 3 years.

## Upsetting the balance

The largemouth bass is highly rated by anglers, and its natural distribution has been artificially increased through introductions to other temperate regions, such as Japan and Europe. Such introductions tend to upset the delicate balance of local food chains. Native animals sometimes have no defenses against the alien predators and therefore suffer heavy predation, with devastating effects on their populations.

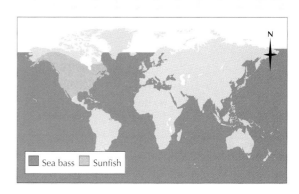

Sea bass ▢ Sunfish

# BAT-EARED FOX

THE BAT-EARED FOX looks rather like a cross between a jackal and a fox. It has a narrow face, extremely large ears, proportionately long legs and a limp, brushlike tail. It is much lighter in build than the common red fox, *Vulpes vulpes*: although the bat-eared fox is almost as long as its more familiar relative, it is only half as heavy. Its coat is yellowish-brown, the long hairs on the shoulders and back tending to fall loosely down either side of the body, leaving a parting in the center. There is a dark streak running through the eyes and down the center of the nose. The limbs are dark, becoming black toward the toes, and the last third of the tail is also black.

## Extraordinary ears

The distinguishing features of the bat-eared fox are its ears, which measure up to 5½ inches (14 cm) long and are brown at the base and black at the tips. The length of the ears is presumed to be an adaptation to life in hot, arid country, whereby the fox is able to lose excess heat through the large surfaces of its ears. The argument for long ears acting as radiators is strengthened by the long ears of the fennec fox, *Fennecus zerda*. This species is the smallest of all the foxes, yet its remarkable ears are 5–6 inches (12.7–15.2 cm) long. It is another resident of hot climates, living in the deserts of North Africa and the Arabian peninsula.

Another feature typical of desert animals is very sensitive hearing. Sometimes this sensitivity is enhanced by adaptations in the mechanisms of the inner ear, as in the North American kangaroo rats of the genus *Dipodomys*, but it can also be improved by a more efficient sound-collecting device. There is reason to suppose that the large ears of the bat-eared and fennec foxes could be primarily connected with their sensitive hearing, with the radiating function as a bonus.

## Intriguing distribution

The bat-eared fox lives in the arid regions of southern and eastern Africa, often favoring open, sandy country. It is found all over southwestern Africa, extending north into Angola and the southern corner of Zimbabwe and south to Port Elizabeth, in Natal. Much further north the species reappears in Ethiopia, Somalia, southern Sudan, Kenya, Tanzania and Uganda. These two discrete populations are located more than 1,000

miles (1,500 km) apart, a rather unusual pattern of distribution. It may be that the current range of the bat-eared fox is all that remains of a much wider distribution in former times. Remains of a now-extinct, closely related species of fox have been found in northwestern India, so the bat-eared fox or its relatives may once have occurred right across eastern Africa and through the Middle East to the Indian subcontinent.

Like the red fox, the bat-eared fox is mainly nocturnal. However, in some regions, especially southern Africa, it is quite usual to see bat-eared foxes during the day. The species has a strong sense of curiosity, often coming near human habitations and watching human activities. Bat-eared foxes are usually seen in ones or twos but they occasionally form small parties of five or six. When inactive, they lie down in tall grass or under bushes and overhanging rocks.

Breeding in the bat-eared fox has been recorded at all times of the year, although most births occur from September to November. Litters vary in size, but two to six cubs is usual. The gestation period is about 2–2½ months and the cubs are born in a burrow, often the disused burrow of an aardvark. Young foxes from one litter often help their parents to raise the next, and if the parents die or are killed the dominant juveniles inherit the family range. Leopards are

*Large ears are thought to help the bat-eared fox keep cool in the African savanna, where there is little shade and daytime temperatures can reach 104° F (40° C).*

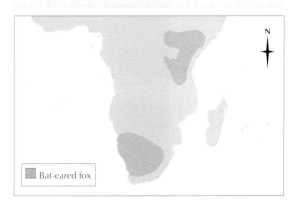

## BAT-EARED FOX

| | |
|---|---|
| CLASS | **Mammalia** |
| ORDER | **Carnivora** |
| FAMILY | **Canidae** |
| GENUS AND SPECIES | ***Otocyon megalotis*** |

WEIGHT
**6–10 lb. (13–22 kg)**

LENGTH
**Head and body: 18–26 in. (46–66 cm); shoulder height: 10–12 in. (25.4–30 cm); tail: 9–13 in. (23–33 cm)**

DISTINCTIVE FEATURES
**Very large, oval-shaped ears; black mask on face; long legs; bushy tail**

DIET
**Mainly termites and beetles, supplemented with other insects, scorpions, small mammals, bird eggs and carrion**

BREEDING
**Breeding season: all year, with births peaking September–November; gestation period: 60–75 days; number of young: 2 to 6**

HABITAT
**Open bush and savanna in arid regions; avoids mountains and woodland**

LIFE SPAN
**Up to 14 years in captivity**

DISTRIBUTION
**Southern and eastern Africa**

STATUS
**Locally common**

☐ Bat-eared fox

*A female bat-eared fox tending a litter of week-old cubs outside her burrow.*

the chief predator of bat-eared foxes. Jackals and hyenas also harass them and they are still hunted by the people of southwestern Africa, who run them down with dogs.

## Insectivorous diet

The bat-eared fox feeds mainly on termites, beetles and other insects. Its very dense fur protects it from the bites of soldier termites. However, the precise diet of the bat-eared fox varies from area to area. Writers who have studied bat-eared foxes in one part of Africa will say that they live almost wholly on termites, whereas others who know another region write that the foxes' diet is more varied, including for example small rodents, the eggs and nestlings of ground-nesting birds and carrion.

The droppings of bat-eared foxes are often found around gerbil warrens, where several families of gerbils have their burrows in a sandy bank. The foxes run down these small rodents, which freeze on being alarmed before scurrying toward their holes. The gerbils can rapidly change direction, suddenly doubling back on their tracks, but the bat-eared foxes are just as skillful at doubling back in pursuit.

## Twin teeth

The predominantly insectivorous diet of the bat-eared fox is reflected in the structure of its teeth. Other members of the dog family have strong teeth with some of the cheek teeth, the carnassials, having sharp edges for cutting off lumps of meat from prey. The bat-eared fox, in contrast, has small and relatively weak teeth.

A more unusual feature of the bat-eared fox is that it has more teeth than any other placental (true) mammal apart from the toothed whales, such as the dolphins. It has an extra tooth on each side of each jaw, lacking in other dogs, which have probably been formed by some of the normal teeth "twinning". This can happen as a freak occurrence in other animals, when teeth of a simple structure are duplicated. Elephants, for instance, sometimes have double tusks. The additional teeth of the bat-eared fox probably help it to crush insects efficiently.

# BATS

THERE ARE NOW more than 900 recognized species of bats. Among mammals, only the rodents are richer in species. Bats exhibit a tremendous range of size. At the bottom end of the scale is the tiny bumblebee bat, *Craseonycteris thonglongyai*, a rare species from Thailand that weighs just ⅒ ounce (2 g) and is one of the world's smallest mammals. The largest bats are two species of flying foxes native to Southeast Asia, *Pteropus giganteus* and *P. vampyrus*, which have wingspans of up to 6½ feet (2 m) and which weigh as much as 3⅓ pounds (1.5 kg).

Bats occur on every continent apart from Antarctica, and exploit a greater range of dietary niches than any other group of mammals. Foods that feature in their various diets include insects and other arthropods, birds, rodents, lizards, smaller bats, fish, fruit, nectar, pollen and blood. Examples of bats with unusual diets are the frog-eating bat, *Trachops cirrhosus*, the fish-eating bat, *Noctilio leporinus*, the fishing bat, *Pizonyx vivesi*, and the three species of vampire bats.

Bats are the only mammals capable of sustained, powered flight. They achieve this with wings developed from immensely elongated fingers, between which a membrane of naked skin is stretched. In many species, the membrane is also stretched between the back legs and tail, increasing the wing size.

*High-speed photographic exposures, in this case of a long-eared bat,* Plecotus auritus, *demonstrate the superb aerial agility typical of many bats.*

## Evolution

The origins and early evolution of the order Chiroptera, or bats, remain obscure. The earliest known fossil bats date back 50 million years. These ancient bats had fully developed flight capabilities, and even possessed advanced echolocation; a biological sonar like that used in submarines. But all of the fossil bats closely resemble modern bats. Unfortunately, scientists do not know of any earlier, more primitive "proto-bats" that would link bats to their first ancestors or to their nearest relatives alive today.

Most scientists believe that bats evolved from an ancient type of nocturnal insectivore that lived in trees. Adding weight to this theory is the fact that 14 of today's 18 bat families are primarily nocturnal insectivores. There are about 625 insect-eating bat species. However, members of the suborder Megachiroptera specialize in eating fruit, nectar and pollen.

Some biologists claim that the Megachiroptera have entirely separate origins from other bats and are actually related to primates. They resemble primitive primates in that they are nocturnal animals that navigate using very large, well-developed eyes. Apart from Egyptian fruit bats in the genus *Rousettus*, megachiropterans cannot echolocate.

## Echolocation

Bats that belong to the larger suborder Microchiroptera are nocturnal but, contrary to popular belief, are not blind. It is more accurate to say that microchiropteran bats are more or less reliant on the sense of echolocation for orientating in flight, for avoiding obstacles and, in most species, for locating, identifying and capturing prey. All this is achieved on the wing in most insectivorous species.

In these bats the sense of echolocation is extremely sophisticated. They emit very high-intensity squeaks at a rate of 3 to 200 per second, sounds that are inaudible to humans because they are pitched too high for human ears to detect. The bats

| CLASSIFICATION |
|---|
| **CLASS** Mammalia |
| **ORDER** Chiroptera |
| **SUBORDER** Megachiroptera: Old World fruit bats  Microchiroptera: all other species of bats |
| **NUMBER OF SPECIES** Approximately 900 |

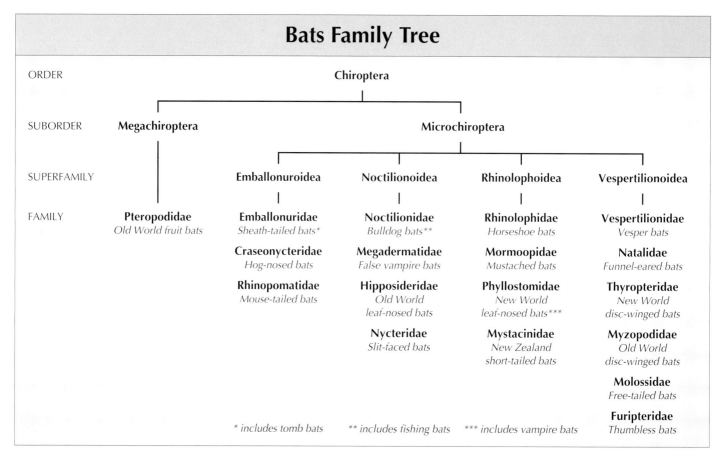

# Bats Family Tree

| ORDER | | | Chiroptera | | |
|---|---|---|---|---|---|

| SUBORDER | Megachiroptera | | Microchiroptera | | |
|---|---|---|---|---|---|

| SUPERFAMILY | | Emballonuroidea | Noctilionoidea | Rhinolophoidea | Vespertilionoidea |
|---|---|---|---|---|---|
| FAMILY | **Pteropodidae**<br>*Old World fruit bats* | **Emballonuridae**<br>*Sheath-tailed bats\** | **Noctilionidae**<br>*Bulldog bats\*\** | **Rhinolophidae**<br>*Horseshoe bats* | **Vespertilionidae**<br>*Vesper bats* |
| | | **Craseonycteridae**<br>*Hog-nosed bats* | **Megadermatidae**<br>*False vampire bats* | **Mormoopidae**<br>*Mustached bats* | **Natalidae**<br>*Funnel-eared bats* |
| | | **Rhinopomatidae**<br>*Mouse-tailed bats* | **Hipposideridae**<br>*Old World<br>leaf-nosed bats* | **Phyllostomidae**<br>*New World<br>leaf-nosed bats\*\*\** | **Thyropteridae**<br>*New World<br>disc-winged bats* |
| | | | **Nycteridae**<br>*Slit-faced bats* | **Mystacinidae**<br>*New Zealand<br>short-tailed bats* | **Myzopodidae**<br>*Old World<br>disc-winged bats* |
| | | | | | **Molossidae**<br>*Free-tailed bats* |
| | | *\* includes tomb bats* | *\*\* includes fishing bats* | *\*\*\* includes vampire bats* | **Furipteridae**<br>*Thumbless bats* |

construct a sound "image" of their surroundings by analyzing features of the returning echoes and by calculating the time delay between the emitted squeak and its echoes.

Most of the apparently bizarre facial features of microchiropteran bats are associated with the functioning of their echolocation systems. Some bats, such as the horseshoe bats in the family Rhinolophidae, emit echolocation calls from their nostrils and use the structures around their noses to focus the beam of sound. Many microchiropterans also have outlandishly large external ears and very sensitive hearing. Examples include the long-eared myotis, *Myotis evotis*, of the western United States and southwestern Canada, the spotted bat, *Euderma maculatum*, of the southern states, and Townsend's big-eared bat, *Plecotus townsendii*, which is found mainly on the West Coast. Some species of bat use their sensitive ears not only in echolocation, but also in listening for faint squeaking or rustling sounds made by their prey.

## Group-living

Female bats typically gather together at the onset of the maternity season, forming colonies that number from a few bats to several million. The males are mainly solitary at this time. During the day, females roost together in the maternity colonies, which are located in safe, concealed places. Common sites include crevices and cavities in caves

*A colony of greater horseshoe bats,* Rhinolophus ferrumequinum. *Roosting bats furl their wings and hang by their hind feet. Hanging for long periods does not cause them any discomfort.*

and mines, inside holes in tree-trunks, among tree foliage and inside artificial structures, especially churches, barns and houses. At dusk, the bats leave the colony to forage.

In some fruit bat species in the suborder Megachiroptera, the young, known as pups, may ride with their mothers. In the Microchiroptera, pups are left behind in the roost, and may huddle together for warmth. The emergence of bats at sunset is a good time to observe them, although it is almost impossible to identify with any certainty a bat seen in flight. Later at night, a special hand-held device called a bat-detector enables humans to hear the ultrasonic echolocation calls, which bats emit all the time while in flight. With sufficient practice it is possible to recognise some species of bat by their echolocation sounds.

## Slow breeders

Most of the bats found in temperate regions have a single pup in early summer. In the Tropics, female bats can give birth at any time of the year provided that there is a plentiful supply of food. Tropical species tend to have young during or shortly after the rains, or when trees are in full fruit, and may have two or three pups a year. Although bats have a very low reproductive rate, they are long-lived for small mammals; a typical life span is up to 30 years.

The energy demand on a mother during the rearing of her pups is huge. In one night, a small female of an insectivorous species regularly eats more than her own weight in insects. The young bats are not independent until their wings are fully grown, at which point they can hunt for themselves. When this occurs, a maternity colony usually disperses. However, a few species of Megachiroptera are strongly colonial and live in the same roost throughout the year.

## Hibernation

In temperate latitudes, including in the United States and most of Canada, bats congregate again at the end of the fall to hibernate. The hibernating bats live off accumulated fat stores, thereby surviving the main period of low food availability. Mating takes place in the fall and winter, with pregnancy itself delayed by one of three methods. A female bat may store her mate's sperm before fertilization has even taken place. Alternatively, she may undergo delayed implantation of the fertilized egg, or else delay the development of the embryo. Just before environmental conditions are appropriate for rearing the pup, which is usually during the spring, the pregnancy continues to its full term.

## Conservation

Bats play a vital role in many ecosystems and therefore deserve special attention from conservationists. They pollinate many economically important trees and plants, such as bananas, and on some islands are the only pollinators of certain plants. Fruit-eating bats can disperse large seeds over great distances. They also disperse "pioneer" species of plants. These plants are then able to colonize remote islands and mainland areas that have been cleared of vegetation. Another vital service, perfomed by insectivorous bats, is the regulation of populations of nocturnal insects. In this way bats control numbers of several important agricultural pests.

*Like many other bats, the ghost bat,* Macroderma gigas, *has an outgrowth on the snout to modify and focus echolocation calls.*

Despite the importance of bats, their populations are declining everywhere. Their ranges are shrinking, and several species have become extinct during the 20th century. The main cause of the decline is the loss of roost sites due to human disturbance, especially tree-felling and the construction or alteration of buildings. Treatment of roof timbers for woodworm is particularly toxic to bats. Sometimes the disturbance is accidental, but the widespread, irrational fear of bats has led to many roost sites being deliberately destroyed.

Among the other threats to bats are habitat destruction, especially deforestation, hedgerow clearance and the draining of freshwater habitats; poisoning by insecticides; collisions with power cables; and hunting for the luxury food market in the southern Pacific. Scientists are still identifying new species of bat, and the possibility remains that some species may die out before they have even been discovered.

*For particular species see:*
- FISH-EATING BAT • FLYING FOX • FRUIT BAT
- HAIRLESS BAT • HORSESHOE BAT • PIPISTRELLE BAT
- TOMB BAT • VAMPIRE BAT • VESPER BAT

# BEAKED WHALE

**Beaked whales dive deep to hunt and to escape predators, reaching depths of up to 1,500 feet (460 m). This is Blainville's beaked whale, Mesoplodon densirostris.**

BY FAR THE least known of all whales and dolphins, the beaked whales are a family of approximately 20 small to medium-sized species. Some are known only from their skulls or from carcasses washed up on the shore, and have never been seen alive. For instance, the Tasman, or Shepherd's, beaked whale, *Tasmacetus sheperdi*, is known from just 20 stranded animals found deposited on the coasts of New Zealand. Such a paucity of information makes it very difficult to judge the size of beaked whale populations or to gauge the precise distribution of each species. The World Conservation Union (I.U.C.N.) lists a total of 15 species as in need of urgent further research. It is also likely that there are more species waiting to be discovered.

There are thought to be five genera of beaked whales. The most familiar, *Hyperoodon*, contains two species that are seen relatively frequently compared to the rest of the family: the northern bottlenose whale, *H. ampullatus*, and the southern bottlenose whale, *H. planifrons*. The other genera of beaked whales are *Tasmacetus* (one species), *Berardius* (two species), *Mesoplodon* (14 species) and *Ziphius* (one species).

## Unique appearance
Beaked whales are related to the sperm whales and have several characters and habits in common with them. However, they are smaller and can be distinguished by a distinct beak like that of dolphins. In some species of beaked whale, such as the pair of bottlenose whales, this beak arises abruptly from a bulbous forehead.

Another feature of beaked whales that separates them from all other whales and dolphins is the absence of a notch between the two tail flukes.

Beaked whales are members of the toothed whales, or Odontoceti. Despite this, teeth are usually absent in females and young. Teeth are most noticeable in males, which generally have one or two teeth in the lower jaw. These do not grow through the gums until the whale is fairly old.

## Past and present slaughter
The two bottlenose whales are easily the best known beaked whales because at one time they were often caught by whalers. Their bulbous foreheads contain a waxy oil, which was once used to lubricate delicate machinery. Tens of thousands of northern bottlenose whales were killed from the mid-19th century until 1977, when the species received full legal protection. Before they were hunted, northern bottlenose whales were fearless and highly inquisitive. Schools would swim up to boats to investigate, and could not be driven away, even by firing guns. Today the whales are extremely wary. Their acute hearing gives them plenty of advance warning of approaching danger.

Baird's beaked whale, *Berardius bairdii*, and Cuvier's beaked whale, *Ziphius cavirostris*, have been hunted in Japanese waters for hundreds of years. Their meat is boiled and their blubber is mixed with fish as animal feed. Small numbers are still taken under the government quota system; official figures state that 40 to 60 Baird's beaked whales are killed by Japan annually.

## Much still to discover
Beaked whales range throughout the warm, temperate and cold seas of the world but they are not found off the shores of Siberia, Arctic Canada or northern Greenland. They generally stay in deeper, oceanic waters and only rarely become stranded, which is one reason for the scant knowledge we have of them. Most sightings are concentrated along deep ocean trenches.

Whalers used to trace the movements of northern bottlenose whales and specimens were made available to scientists. The whales migrate north in spring, keeping to the Gulf Stream that runs up into the Arctic Sea, and in summer they can be seen among the ice floes. In September they return south, but it is not known where they

## BOTTLENOSE WHALES

| | |
|---|---|
| CLASS | **Mammalia** |
| ORDER | **Cetacea** |
| FAMILY | **Ziphiidae** |

GENUS AND SPECIES    **Northern bottlenose whale, *Hyperoodon ampullatus*; southern bottlenose whale, *H. planifrons***

ALTERNATIVE NAMES
**Northern bottlenose whale: North Atlantic bottlenose whale; flathead; bottlehead; steephead; southern bottlenose whale: Antarctic bottlenose whale**

WEIGHT
**5950–7940 lb. (2,700–3,600 kg)**

LENGTH
**23–29½ ft. (7–9 m); male larger than female**

DISTINCTIVE FEATURES
**Bulbous forehead; gray body with creamy brown or pale gray underside**

DIET
**Mainly cuttlefish and squid; some fish, especially herring and deep-sea species**

BREEDING
**Age at first breeding: estimated 11 years; breeding season: unknown; number of young: 1; gestation period: about 360 days; breeding interval: probably 2 years**

LIFE SPAN
**Probably 30–40 years**

HABITAT
**Seas deeper than 3,000 ft. (1,000 m)**

DISTRIBUTION
**Northern bottlenose whale: North Atlantic and North Sea; southern bottlenose whale: Southern Hemisphere oceans, north as far as South Africa and southern Australia**

STATUS
**Vulnerable; population unknown**

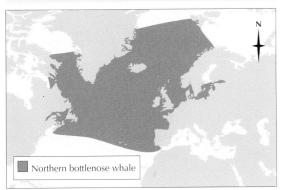

Northern bottlenose whale

spend the winter. Other species of beaked whale are also migratory, although the details of their migrations remain sketchy.

It appears that male northern bottlenose whales travel in separate schools, or parties, from the females and young. There are usually 4 to 12 whales in a school. However, schools of males and females may associate in groups of hundreds of individuals, which are reputedly led by an old male. Legend stated that bottlenose whales remain with their wounded comrades.

Gestation in beaked whales lasts 10 months to a year, and the single calf is usually born during spring or summer. Calves are suckled for 5–7 months in bottlenose whales. Chief among the predators of beaked whales are killer whales, which are escaped by diving to great depths where killer whales cannot follow.

Valuable insights into the diet of beaked whales have been gained by examining the stomach contents of stranded whales. The whales seem to feed almost exclusively on cuttlefish and squid. Prey is caught and held by the beak's horny internal surface, the texture of which has been compared with that of a rough bath towel. When there are teeth present, these must help the whale to grip its prey, which is caught at all depths from the surface to deep water.

*Much of what we know about beaked whales has been gleaned by studying dead specimens washed on to beaches, such as this Cuvier's beaked whale, Ziphius cavirostris.*

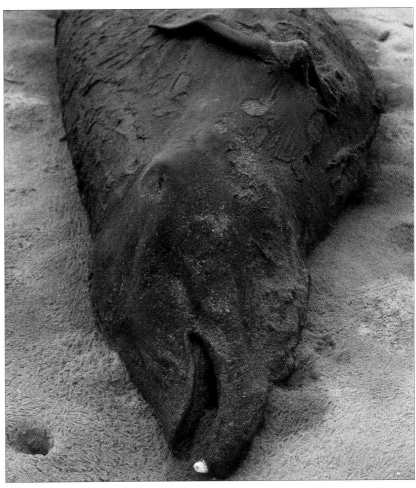

# BEARDED LIZARD

*When attacked, bearded lizards perform a dramatic threat display to persuade the predator to leave them alone.*

THE ENTIRE UPPER surface of bearded lizards is studded with small, spinelike scales, and a jaw pouch forms a shield around the snout. When swollen, the pouch resembles a beard. It is more strongly developed in males than in females and tends to be smaller in lizards living inland. Males are larger than females.

There are seven species of bearded lizards, all native to Australia. They are stout-bodied members of the agamid family, with a long head and a whiplike tail. Their body color ranges from grayish to yellow, depending on their behavioral state. When injured, sick or dying their backs turn black and their legs pale yellow. The lizards' coloration also depends on their surroundings, becoming more intense in drier habitats.

## Arid terrain specialists

Bearded lizards occur in much of Australia, although the commonest species, *Pogona barbata*, is restricted to the east and south. The lizards inhabit arid, sparsely forested country, as well as scrub, semideserts and shorelines. They thrive in hot climates with a daytime temperature of 86–104° F (30–40° C), and hardly move when their body temperature falls below this range.

Bearded lizards are able to survive for several hours even higher temperatures at which other lizards risk getting heatstroke. This is because they can regulate their body temperature by evaporation and because their rate of water loss is low. Basking is another method of temperature regulation. To bask, the lizards climb on to a tree trunk, stump or termite mound, and flatten themselves out in the sun, staying like this for several hours. Nevertheless, the margin between survival and death from heatstroke may be very small.

Bearded lizards are largely insectivorous, but supplement their invertebrate prey with a variety of fruits and ground blossoms, and occasionally with smaller lizards and snakes. As in other lizards, their ears not only pick up sound waves in the air, but also detect vibrations from the ground. Vibrations are transmitted to the ears through the bones of the lower jaw, which for this reason is often held close to the ground.

## Visual threats

A highly developed "language" of impressive visual threats has earned bearded lizards the alternative name of bearded dragons. When cornered, or facing a rival in dispute over territory, a bearded lizard performs an aggressive display. It expands its body by raising its ribs, erects the beard by distending the jaw pouch, opens its mouth to show the golden yellow to yellowish-green tongue and interior of the mouth, and hisses like a snake. This is a warning display: the lizard rarely bites. More often it will attempt concealment by remaining still and changing color.

## Elaborate courtship

Breeding involves a ritualized series of courtship displays. The female bearded lizard develops a red patch at the base of her tail, and the male displays a green patch in the same place. The male also turns black on the underside, from belly to throat, and his back acquires an eye-catching pattern incorporating mottled gray, yellow and bright green. The male blows out his body and opens his mouth from time to time, showing the bright yellow interior.

As the display nears its climax the male stamps with his forefeet, making a surprisingly loud sound, jerks his head up and down and stretches his beard to the full. He runs round in front of the female and positions himself at right angles, about 2 feet (60 cm) in front of her.

# BEARDED LIZARDS

| | |
|---|---|
| CLASS | **Reptilia** |
| ORDER | **Squamata** |
| FAMILY | **Agamidae** |
| GENUS | ***Pogona*** **(formerly *Amphibolurus*)** |
| SPECIES | **7, including *P. barbata* and *P. vitticeps*** |

ALTERNATIVE NAMES
**Bearded dragon; Jew lizard**

LENGTH
**Head and body: up to 10 in. (25 cm);
tail: up to 15¾ in. (40 cm)**

DISTINCTIVE FEATURES
**Large, beardlike appendage beneath lower
jaw; spiny scales on upper surface**

DIET
**Mainly insects; also fruits, flowers, smaller
lizards and small snakes**

BREEDING
**Varies according to species. Number of
eggs: 8 to 24 (*P. barbata*).**

LIFE SPAN
**Probably 10–15 years**

HABITAT
**Wide variety of semiarid and scrub habitats**

DISTRIBUTION
**Australia; range varies according to species**

STATUS
**Most species locally common**

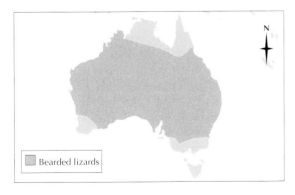

Bearded lizards

*Bearded lizards
specialize in the
"sit and wait" method
of hunting, and lie in
ambush for passing
large insects.*

## A day in the life

Cold-blooded animals, such as the bearded lizard, must rely almost wholly on behavioral controls to keep cool. They lack sweat glands and so cannot lose heat by sweating, and have few other physiological means of controlling body temperature. Like other lizards, bearded lizards therefore follow a daily routine to avoid overheating or dying of cold.

When the sun rises the air is cool, and the bearded lizard responds by turning its back to the sun and exposing as much of its body to the warming rays as possible. As the air warms up so does the lizard's body, and it becomes active. But when the air temperature reaches about 104° F (40° C), the lizard must seek shade under a rock or bush, or in a burrow.

As the day wears on the air begins to cool, but the ground retains its heat. The lizard, now emerged from its retreat, turns its head toward the sun to take in the minimum heat from it, raises its tail to keep it off the hot ground and stands up on its legs with only the toes of the forefeet and the heels of the hindfeet touching the scorching earth. Finally, as both the air and ground cool down and the sun is starting to set, the lizard basks once again.

Bearded lizards often flee predators by rising on their hind legs and running bipedally. It looks as if they are trying to make faster speed. But they do this only when the air temperature is high. They are not trying to accelerate but are countering the heat generated in running by lifting their bodies up from the hot ground.

Repetition of these actions, with variations, may continue for some time before mating finally occurs. After mating, the female scoops a hole in the ground and buries herself in it. She lays her eggs, which are connected by a membrane, leaves the hole and covers them with sand. The young hatch about 3 months later, depending on the species and environmental conditions.

# BEARS

*The grizzly bear,* Ursus arctos, *is the brown bear of North America. This mother will teach her cubs how to fish. Rivers are an easy and abundant source of food for brown bears.*

THE BEAR FAMILY, URSIDAE, belongs to the order Carnivora, which includes all of the typical meat-eating mammals, such as the cats and the dogs. Like the other families in Carnivora, bears have carnassial teeth, molars that are adapted for shearing and slicing flesh. Unlike most carnivores, however, bears include large amounts of vegetable matter in their diet. Indeed, the spectacled bear and the giant panda are almost entirely vegetarian, only rarely eating small animals and fish. The only predominantly carnivorous species of bear is the polar bear, which actively hunts seals along the southern edge of the Arctic pack ice.

Members of the bear family share a number of physical characteristics, in addition to the carnassial teeth common to all carnivores. Bears are all large-bodied animals, weighing 60–1,720 pounds (27–780 kg), and have relatively short limbs and tails. They also have a flat-footed, or plantigrade, stance; the five toes and the heel are placed flush against the ground. This position is unlike that of the cats and the dogs, which stand on only their four front toes, an adaptation for fast running. Bears do not need to run quickly in order to hunt for food. Instead, their plantigrade stance gives them increased mobility, enabling them to use their paws to catch fish or dig for food and shelter.

There are three modern genera of bears. The largest, *Ursus*, contains six species, the brown, black, polar, sloth and sun bears and the Asiatic black bear. The other two genera, *Tremarctos* and *Ailuropoda*, each contain a single species, the spectacled bear and the giant panda respectively.

## Prehistoric bears

The earliest known ancestor of the bear family was a wolfhound-sized carnivore, *Cephalogale*, fossils of which were found in Chinese rocks dating back 37 million years. However, the progenitor of today's genus *Ursus* was an animal called *Ursavus elmensis*. Slightly smaller than *Cephalogale*, this prehistoric bear appeared over 20 million years ago and probably lived in a similar way to the sun bears of modern Southeast Asia. It was likely to have been a proficient tree-climber, with a varied diet that included fruit, shoots, insects, birds and small mammals.

The descendants of *Ursavus* remained small until 2½ million years ago, when larger species start to appear in the fossil record. The increase in size might have been triggered by the onset of the Ice Age. Large animals are more efficient at retaining heat than small ones, and there may have been a strong natural selection for a large body size.

The group of bears that eventually gave rise to the giant panda was the first to split from the ancestral bear. Another group of bears was to diverge at a later date, perhaps as a response to a change in habitat, from humid forests to temperate forests and scrubland, brought about by a drier climate. This group, known as the running bears, abandoned a forest-dwelling existence and an omnivorous diet (one that includes both animal and plant matter). Some species became giant, meat-eating hunters. But almost all of the running bears had died out by 10,000 years ago. Their sole survivor is the spectacled bear of South America, which shows little resemblance to its ancestors.

## Larger males

Much bear behavior can be explained by the animals' large size. Bears require a lot of food, and must therefore travel considerable distances in search of new feeding opportunities. Female brown bears of the inland regions of North America, for example,

| CLASSIFICATION | | |
| --- | --- | --- |
| **CLASS** Mammalia | | |
| **ORDER** Carnivora | | |
| **FAMILY** Ursidae | | |
| **NUMBER OF SPECIES** 8 | | |

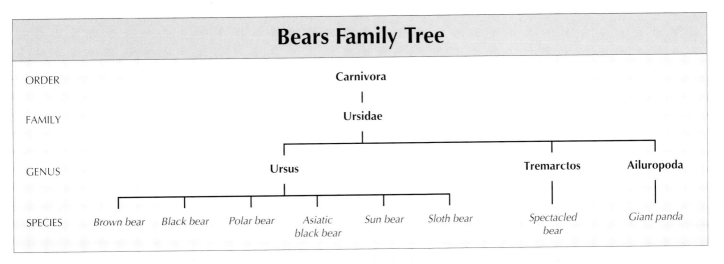

# Bears Family Tree

| ORDER | | | | Carnivora | | | | | |
|---|---|---|---|---|---|---|---|---|---|
| FAMILY | | | | Ursidae | | | | | |
| GENUS | | | Ursus | | | | | Tremarctos | Ailuropoda |
| SPECIES | Brown bear | Black bear | Polar bear | Asiatic black bear | Sun bear | Sloth bear | | Spectacled bear | Giant panda |

may cover areas of up to 80 square miles (200 sq km). Since female bears range so widely, males do not establish and defend territories in the manner of many other carnivores. They instead wander far and wide in an attempt to find as many potential mates as possible. It is not uncommon for the home ranges of several males to overlap, the owners of which fight to have priority over receptive females. A consequence of this aggressive competition for mates is that male bears are often considerably larger than females of the same species. Male black bears and Asiatic black bears can be up to 70–80 percent heavier than females.

## Deep sleep

Being so large, bears cannot find enough food in winter to satisfy their large appetites and thus remain active. The survival strategy that bears have adopted is to enter a deep sleep in the fall and rest until spring. During the fall, when food is plentiful, bears gorge themselves to build up fat reserves. With the onset of cold weather they retire to a den excavated in the ground, within an existing cavity in a tree or hidden among rocks. The bears' heart rate and body temperature fall corresponding to a decrease in their metabolic rate.

This state is not true hibernation, and sleeping bears are easily woken. If a predator discovers the den, the bear can easily defend itself. Bears found in tropical or subtropical climates, such as the sun bear and many of the black bears living in the southern United States, do not enter a deep sleep at all and are able to stay active throughout the year.

## Winter births

Female bears give birth while still in the winter den. There are usually one to four cubs in a litter, and by the time they are born the female will have been without food and water for many weeks. For this reason newly born bear cubs are very small; each weighs less than 10 percent of the weight that would be predicted for a mammal of the female's size. The mother continues fasting while she feeds the cubs.

Females of all bear species rear their cubs alone, feeding them on rich, viscous milk until they leave the den and begin foraging. This is in contrast to many other carnivores, the males of which bring food for both the females and young. Even after bear cubs have started finding food for themselves their mother will continue nursing them until they leave her home range and become independent. The cubs remain under her protection for 1–2 years.

*Male polar bears, Ursus maritimus, play-fighting. Unlike other species of bear, the polar bear remains active all winter, although it retreats to temporary dens in severe weather.*

*A black bear in its den. In winter food shortages make it necessary for most bears to enter a deep sleep until the following spring, during which they lose up to half of their body weight.*

## Bear necessities

Bears live a mostly solitary existence, coming together only during the mating season or where food is plentiful, such as at salmon streams. This is because the food that bears eat is not often found in large quantities and would not be enough to feed a group, or sloth, of bears.

Groups of polar bears can be seen during the summer on the western coast of Hudson Bay. They gather here waiting for the sea to freeze over again so that they can walk across the ice to hunt seals. Most bears are opportunist meat-eaters as well as active predators, sometimes carefully stalking their prey in order to avoid having to run quickly over long distances. The young of animals such as moose or deer are easier prey than the adults since they are not able to run as quickly.

Bears in temperate and Arctic areas must store up enough fat during the summer and fall months to ensure survival during the winter sleep, when there is little or no food. They may double or triple their weight, storing a thick layer of fat under their skin, which gives them a very bulky appearance. This probably also provides them with a layer of insulation. When the bear reemerges from its long sleep it may weigh just 50 percent of its fall body weight.

In the spring the bear must once again begin to eat the large quantities of food necessary to survive the next winter. In order to obtain enough food, bears may have to roam over very large home ranges and must be able to remember exactly where food may be available at particular times of year. Bears are excellent navigators, possibly using the earth's magnetic field to find their way. In North America, bears that are taken away from areas where they are a nuisance to the public are able find their way back home over distances of well over

125 miles (200 km). In Alaska male brown bears may roam home ranges of several hundred square miles.

## Bears and humans

Black bears are not considered dangerous to humans. They are sometimes attracted to campsites, picnic areas or houses where there is potential food in garbage. In such situations they do not often pose a threat and will probably ignore humans, only attacking if they feel threatened. If, however, they have become accustomed to being fed and find that there is no food, they may attack.

By far the most dangerous species of bear is the polar bear, which will attack humans as prey, rather than because it has come to expect to be fed or because it has been surprised. Generally, however, humans pose more of a threat to bears than bears to humans. In cases where bears show aggression or are felt to be potentially dangerous to humans, they are often shot.

## Decreasing populations

In historic times bears were found throughout Eurasia and North America, in the Atlas Mountains of North Africa and in the Andes of South America. The populations of all eight species of modern bears have greatly decreased over the last thousand years. This has been due mainly to habitat loss, brought about by the spread of agriculture, and to hunting and persecution by humans. Bear populations grow very slowly because bears are not sexually mature until 2½–6 years of age and adult females have litters only once every 1–4 years. Once a bear population has declined it takes a considerable length of time for it to recover its previous size.

Four species of bears have been categorized by the I.U.C.N. (World Conservation Union) as vulnerable, threatened or endangered. These are the Asiatic black, sloth and spectacled bears and the giant panda. No more than 1,000 giant pandas now survive in the wild. Insufficient data are available on the status of the sun bear, although the species is likely also to be threatened through habitat and range fragmentation. Careful management of wilderness areas and a significant change in attitude toward large predators are needed to ensure the continued existence of bears.

*For particular species see:*
- ASIATIC BLACK BEAR • BLACK BEAR • BROWN BEAR
- GIANT PANDA • POLAR BEAR • SLOTH BEAR
- SPECTACLED BEAR • SUN BEAR

# BEAVER

Beavers are the second largest type of rodent, exceeded in size only by the capybara. Stout-bodied, with a large, thickset head and powerful limbs, a beaver can weigh as much as 85 pounds (38.5 kg). It has a blunt muzzle, small ears and five toes on each foot. Those on the front feet are strongly clawed for digging, manipulating food and carrying mud or stones for building. The hind feet are webbed, with two split claws for grooming the fur and spreading water-proofing oil. The beaver's body oil also provides insulation against the cold, as do its dense layer of underfur and its heavy outer coat of coarse hairs, known as guard hairs.

When a beaver submerges, its nostrils and ears are automatically closed by valves, and it can remain underwater for 15 minutes. The tail is used for steering and sometimes for propulsion through the water. It also forms a tripod with the hind legs when the beaver stands up to gnaw trees.

## Pair of species

There are two species of beaver, which resemble each other closely in both appearance and habits. The Canadian beaver once occurred throughout North America, from northern Canada south to beyond the United States–Mexico border. Today it is found in severely depleted numbers from Canada into parts of the northern United States. The European beaver must at one time have been plentiful throughout Europe, but has long been extinct in England and survives in relatively small numbers elsewhere, mainly in Scandinavia, on rivers in European Russia and in the valleys of the rivers Elbe and Rhône. However, where it has been given protection, the species shows signs of increasing.

## Waterside lodges

Beavers live in loose colonies comprising a family unit of four to eight, or sometimes up to 12, individuals. Each colony has a dominant breeding pair, which mates for life, and the young remain with their parents for 2 years. The colony's home is either a burrow dug into a bank, with an underwater entrance, or a lodge in a beaver pond, a pool made by damming a river until it overflows. The beavers make secondary dams upstream of the lodge to help control the flow of water and relieve some of the strain from the main dam, and usually add another sec-

ondary dam downstream of their pond. They obtain the branches they need for building by felling young trees, using their chisel-like incisors to chew chips out of the trunks until the trees fall. The beavers cut the trees up and carry the timber to the building site. If necessary, they dig canals to float logs to the pond.

## Feats of engineering

The typical beaver lodge is a conical pile of logs, branches and sticks compacted with mud and stones. It may reach 36 feet (11 m) in width, and its upper section projects up to 2½ feet (2 m) above the water surface. From an engineering standpoint, the beaver lodge could hardly be improved. It has a central chamber just above water level, one or more escape tunnels leading from the chamber to underwater exits and well-insulated walls. A vertical chimney or ventilating shaft helps to regulate the internal temperature and provides air-conditioning.

Evidence gained from dissecting beaver lodges suggests that they are built by laying sticks more or less horizontally to create a pile. The beavers then chew their way inside to make the entrance tunnels and the central chamber. Finally they add a surface cladding of mud and stones, but stop short about 1 foot (30 cm) from the top of the pile so that the spaces between the sticks provide ventilation.

Beaver dams give way no more frequently than do artificial dams. This is because they are resilient, under constant surveillance, subject to immediate repair and supported by subsidiary

*In beavers the jaw bone is unusually wide to accommodate the the large muscles they need for gnawing wood. This European beaver is stripping bark from a felled branch.*

*Beaver dams (above) and lodges provide excellent examples of a species manipulating its environment for its own benefit.*

## BEAVERS

| | |
|---|---|
| CLASS | **Mammalia** |
| ORDER | **Rodentia** |
| FAMILY | **Castoridae** |

GENUS AND SPECIES **Canadian beaver, *Castor canadensis*; European beaver, *C. fiber***

WEIGHT
**Up to 85 lb. (38.5 kg), usually 25–55 lb. (11–25 kg)**

LENGTH
**Head and body: 24–36 in. (61–92 cm); tail: 10–18 in. (25.5–46 cm)**

DISTINCTIVE FEATURES
**Large incisor teeth; thickset head; stocky body; muscular limbs with strong claws; very broad, flattened and scaly tail**

DIET
**Bark, shoots and leaves of birch, aspen and willow; some aquatic vegetation**

BREEDING
**Age at first breeding: 1–3 years; breeding season: January–June; gestation period: 100–110 days; number of young: usually 2 to 4; breeding interval: 1 year**

LIFE SPAN
**Up to 24 years, usually 7–8 years**

HABITAT
**Lakes, rivers and streams in or near to deciduous woodland, preferably with birch or aspen trees**

DISTRIBUTION
**Canadian beaver: throughout North America. European beaver: patchy range in northern and central Europe and the former U.S.S.R.**

STATUS
**Canadian beaver: abundant in north of range, common to uncommon elsewhere. European beaver: rather uncommon.**

Beavers

dams. Main dams average 25 yards (23 m) in length, but in exceptional cases may stretch for up to 600 yards (550 m) from end to end.

Many people think that beavers are unusually intelligent, largely because their lodges and dams display such fine engineering work. In fact, beavers are instinctive builders following an inborn pattern of behavior. A colony of beavers that occupied an artificial dam made of concrete and stone on a small lake in New York State set about repairing the dam with branches and mud even although it was already fully effective and there was no chance of a leak.

## High-fiber diet

Beavers eat the bark, sapwood, shoots and leaves of twigs and small branches, including those cut during building work. They prefer aspen and willow, but also feed on birch and a range of other deciduous trees. The wood that beavers eat is remarkably nutritious. This is because food made in the leaves of a tree is carried in the sap just below the bark, where most of the tree cells that are alive and growing—and therefore contain protein—are also concentrated.

Beavers often store surplus twigs and branches around the base of their lodge. These have always been regarded as being for the winter use of all members of the colony but recent research has shown that the bulk of these are eaten by the young and that older beavers live on their fat and eat little during winter.

## Life at the lodge

Beavers are monogamous, and the mating season lasts from January to February. The female gives birth to a litter of two to four young, or sometimes more, in April, May or early June. The young, or kits, have a coat of soft fur and open eyes. At birth each weighs about ½–1 pounds (225–450 g) and is 15 inches (38 cm) long, including 3½ inches (9 cm) of tail. Kits start to find and eat solid food at 1 month, but are not weaned until 6 weeks old. They remain with their parents for about 2 years, becoming sexually mature at 1–3 years of age.

As with all rodents, beavers are hunted by many predators of approximately their own weight or more. Their enemies include the wolverine, lynx, coyote, gray wolf, bobcat, puma and brown bear. A beaver's alarm signal when a predator is in sight is to bring the tail over the back then smack it down with such force on the water that the sound can be heard up to ½ miles (0.8 km) away. Beavers can make fearsome opponents when cornered, turning in their tracks to face the enemy, with the hair on their head and neck standing on end.

## Decline of the European beaver

European beavers were on the way to extinction in the 19th century as a result of centuries of hunting by humans. Their extermination was due partly to their valuable fur—beaver pelts were up to six times as valuable as marten, otter, wolf and fox pelts—but particularly to slaughter for the glandular secretion with which beavers mark their territories. This secretion, known as castoreum, enjoyed a vogue as a cure-all in the 16th and 17th centuries. Scientific analysis has shown castoreum to contain salicylic acid, one of the ingredients of aspirin.

Beavers were once common in Switzerland, as shown by the place-names Biberach, Bibersee and Biberstein (*Biber* is German for beaver). Their former presence in England, too, is commemorated by such place-names as Beverley, Beverege, Bevercotes and Beversbrook. The species seems to have survived in Britain until the mid-16th century. At this time Henry IV of France, impressed by the demand for beaver

*A Canadian beaver feeding on willow twigs in the relative safety of its pond.*

pelts for hats, trimmings, fur linings and leather for shoes, tried to increase the economic strength of his state by sending troops to Newfoundland and Nova Scotia. In due course the English gained control of this resource, largely through the Hudson Bay Trading Company. It was the search for more furs that led to new areas of Canada being explored by Europeans.

## Profit or protection?

The Hudson Bay Trading Company was formed in 1670, and such was the growth of its trade that from 1853 to 1877 it marketed nearly 3 million beaver pelts. Whereas Native Americans killed only mature animals, so that their hunting had little impact on beaver populations, the new trappers killed beavers indiscriminately. Within 150 years the Canadian beaver had been exterminated in the coastal regions of the eastern states, and seriously reduced elsewhere. As more of the North American continent was opened up, so the trade continued unabated, with results similar to those seen in the eastern states.

Beavers were not always killed for profit. At times they became a nuisance by making inroads on timber, invading settled areas, damaging riverbanks and feeding on corn. Nevertheless, the species received legal protection in Maine as early as 1866. By the early 20th century its numbers had increased to such an extent that population controls had to be imposed again. Many beaver conservation initiatives have since been undertaken by landowners, public bodies and state and federal governments. This is because the authorities realized that beaver ponds and dams on the headwaters of mountain streams hold back large quantities of water during the dangerous flood season and equalize the water flow so that during the dry seasons the water supply is greatly increased in the valleys.

# BEE-EATER

*Bee-eaters hunt large insects on the wing and return to a convenient perch to consume their prey. This rainbow bee-eater has caught a dragonfly.*

and golden upperparts, a blue breast and belly, a bright yellow throat and a greenish-blue tail. Even the relatively dull species of bee-eater have at least some patches of bright color.

The flight of bee-eaters is also highly characteristic. A flock will circle around for considerable lengths of time, each bird flapping rapidly then gliding buoyantly on outstretched, pointed wings, and all the time calling with a liquid, insistent, twittering.

## Birds of warm climates

Bee-eaters live mainly in tropical regions, and the greatest variety is found in Africa. In many parts of the Tropics, flocks of hundreds, or occasionally even thousands, of bee-eaters can be seen wheeling and gliding over their nesting colonies and feeding grounds, a most impressive sight. A few species, such as the European bee-eater, live in milder, temperate areas. Several are migratory, moving toward the tropics outside the breeding season. The rainbow bee-eater, for example, migrates to New Guinea and the Celebes, while the species found on Madagascar crosses to mainland Africa for the winter.

In the 1940s the European bee-eater began to expand its range northward from southern Europe. It spread from southern France, northern Italy, the former Yugoslavia, Hungary and Romania north to the Czech Republic, where it bred in 1948, and to Denmark, Belgium and northern France, where a few pairs bred in the 1950s. Three pairs nested in Sussex in the south of England in 1955, but the range expansion was short-lived. Bee-eaters thrive only where there is an abundant supply of large insects, and due to this dietary preference they must avoid those latitudes that have short, wet summers and long, cool winters.

## Insectivorous feeders

For the most part, bee-eaters feed on flying insects, catching them on the wing. They hunt by circling around and by waiting on a suitable lookout, such as a branch or telegraph wire, and darting away from the perch to catch passing prey. This perch may be a branch, or an animal. The chief food of bee-eaters is dragonflies,

B EE-EATERS ARE AMONG the most colorful birds of the Old World. There are 26 species, found across much of southern Europe, Africa and Madagascar, southern Asia, Indonesia, Southeast Asia and Australia. They measure 6–14 inches (15–36 cm) from head to tail and most species display strong color contrasts, in which green often predominates, with shades of yellow, blue and red adding to the pattern. The Australian species, *Merops ornatus*, has been aptly named the rainbow bee-eater, or rainbow bird. The European bee-eater, *M. apiaster*, one of the most widespread members of the family, has chestnut

# EUROPEAN BEE-EATER

CLASS **Aves**

ORDER **Coraciiformes**

FAMILY **Meropidae**

GENUS AND SPECIES **Merops apiaster**

WEIGHT
**1½–2¾ oz. (44–78 g)**

LENGTH
**Head to tail: 10½–12 in. (27–30 cm);
wingspan: 17–19 in. (44–49 cm)**

DISTINCTIVE FEATURES
**Long, decurved bill; bright plumage with
strong color contrasts; long, blue-green tail
with even longer pair of central feathers**

DIET
**Mainly large flying insects, especially bees,
wasps, beetles, butterflies and dragonflies;
supplemented with some terrestrial and
aquatic invertebrates**

BREEDING
**Age at first breeding: 1–2 years; breeding
season: eggs laid May–June; number of
eggs: 6 or 7; incubation period: 20 days;
fledging period: 20–33 days; breeding
interval: 1 year**

LIFE SPAN
**Not known**

HABITAT
**Open country with scattered trees; sandy
banks, often beside rivers and highways,
used for nesting**

DISTRIBUTION
**Breeds from Portugal, Spain and
northwestern Africa east to Central Asia
and the northern Middle East, and in South
Africa. Winters in sub-Saharan Africa.**

STATUS
**Generally common**

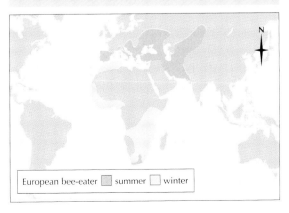

European bee-eater ▢ summer ▢ winter

beetles, butterflies, wasps and bees. It has been estimated that some European bee-eaters can catch more than 225 insects in one day. In Africa the bee-eaters are helpful to humans by taking a large toll of locusts.

Bee-eaters also have a range of more unusual hunting strategies. For instance, the carmine bee-eater, *M. nubicus*, of sub-Saharan Africa, often rides on the backs of bustards, leaving its mobile perch at regular intervals to catch insects that the large ground birds disturb while they walk about. Bee-eaters in different parts of the world have often been reported as plunging into rivers and emerging with food, presumably freshwater insects and crustaceans.

## Breeding burrows

A bee-eater nest is typically a burrow dug with bill and feet in sandy banks and cliffs by the sides of rivers and roads. The tunnel is 2–3 inches (5–8 cm) in diameter and 2–5 feet (0.6–1.5 m) long, or sometimes up to 8 feet (2.5 m), depending on the softness of the soil. Many species of bee-eater breed in colonies, and thousands of nests may be constructed close to one another. In Africa nesting chambers are often made in the abandoned burrows of aardvarks.

Burrowing starts with the bee-eater flying repeatedly at the wall with its bill partly open. When a sufficient hole has been made, the bird can perch at the edge and dig more rapidly. Excavation takes from between 10 days to 2 weeks and the tunnel ends with a chamber, usually set off to one side. No nest is made, although a pile of insect remains builds up as the bee-eaters eject pellets composed of the indigestible parts of their meals. The eggs are laid on

*The European
bee-eater nests
in colonies. It digs
downward-sloping
tunnels in sandy
banks, at the end
of which it builds
a nesting chamber.*

*Little bee-eaters,*
**Merops pusillus,** *are a common sight across much of Africa.*

## Job-sharing

Bee-eaters usually produce only one brood of eggs per year. Incubation takes about 20 days in the European bee-eater, with each parent sitting for spells of 10–30 minutes. The female generally spends the night on the eggs while the male roosts in a tree. During incubation the male feeds his mate, and when the chicks have hatched, both parents feed them. The male bee-eater also brings back food for the female. Parent bee-eaters are helped in their task, usually by 1-year old birds from the brood of the previous year. Fledging is complete in about 3 weeks.

Unusually among birds, each feather of a bee-eater nestling is retained in a membrane until the bird is nearly full grown, at which point the feather bursts out. The chicks may wander some distance from the nesting chamber but usually return there to roost at night.

Snakes and lizards are probably important predators of most bee-eater species. They crawl down burrows to steal the eggs and young, and even the adults. Birds of prey also pose a threat. Flocks of bee-eaters take communal action, swooping down on their enemy to drive it away from the colony. In southern France the European bee-eater's main predators are the Montpellier snake (*Malpolon monspessulanus*), ocellated lizard (*Lacerta lepida*) and black kite (*Milvus migrans*).

## Avoiding being stung

Stinging insects are an important item in the diet of bee-eaters and the question arises as to how the birds avoid being stung. It is possible that bee-eaters are in fact stung and that they are immune to bee and wasp venom. However, observations made of bee-eaters suggest that instead they take steps to avoid the insect stings in the first place.

Bee-eaters usually pick up bees and wasps with the tip of their bills, holding the insects at the narrow "waist." They rap the head of the insect against the perch a few times, shift their grip to the end of the abdomen, just behind the sting, and rub it vigorously against the perch. This procedure usually results in the sting being torn out or, if not, the venom is probably squeezed out. The victim is again held by the "waist" and beaten against the perch, then tossed to the back of the bill and swallowed.

This sequence of events appears to be invariable whenever bee-eaters are feeding on stinging insects. Other, defenseless prey items are swallowed immediately or as soon as they have been hammered to stop their struggling. Young bee-eaters are clumsy at first and sometimes get stung. However, it seems that the young are partly immune to quantities of venom that would be sufficient to kill other birds.

this organic debris. The burrows are used from year to year, being refurbished by having some of the insect remains removed.

In the Camargue, the marshy delta of the Rhône River on the Mediterranean coast of France, European bee-eaters arrive from their African winter quarters in April or early May. Breeding takes place in late May and June. The nesting burrows usually face south, thus avoiding the severity of the seasonal Mediterranean wind called the mistral.

Before eggs are laid, each pair of European bee-eaters vigorously defends a favored perch in a nearby tree against the other bee-eaters in the colony. The reason for this territorial behavior, unconnected with either feeding or the nest, is not known. It may be to allow courtship and mating to proceed undisturbed, for once the eggs are laid the aggressive behavior ends.

The European bee-eater lays up to 10 white eggs. Most burrow-nesting birds, including the other species of bee-eater, also lay white eggs. This is presumably because there is no evolutionary pressure to develop a camouflage to keep the clutches hidden from predators. It has been suggested that the white eggs of bee-eaters act as reflectors so that the adults can see more clearly in the burrow. However, this is an unlikely explanation as the burrows are often crooked, and so pitch-black. Moreover, accidental destruction of the eggs by parent birds is frequent.

# BEES AND WASPS

**B**EES AND WASPS ARE members of an extremely diverse order of insects, the Hymenoptera, which also includes the ants and the sawflies. There are more than 120,000 recognized species in this order, and it is likely that there are thousands more yet to be identified and described.

Every species in the order Hymenoptera has chewing mouthparts and two pairs of transparent wings. The pair of hind wings are smaller than the pair of forewings and are joined to the forewings by a series of small hooks. However, bees and wasps differ from the other insects in the order Hymenoptera in that they have a constricted "waist" formed from sections of the abdomen.

## Classification
Both bees and wasps belong to the suborder Apocrita. *Bee* is a general term applied to the superfamily Apoidae. This group contains many well-known species, such as honeybees and bumblebees, that exhibit social behavior and live in large colonies. However, most species, such as the bees in the genera *Chelostoma* and *Andrena*, are solitary.

*Wasp* is another generalized name. It refers to the true wasps, in the superfamily Vespoidea, and also to a variety of parasitic species in the superfamily Parasitica. Some wasps are social but, like bees, most species have a solitary lifestyle.

## A sting in the tail
Female bees and wasps possess an ovipositor, a tubelike organ at the end of the abdomen through which they lay their eggs. In some species, however, the ovipositor is adapted into a sting that is capable of delivering a painful or even paralyzing dose of venom. Male bees and wasps lack ovipositors, and thus also lack stings.

Parasitic wasps, such as the ichneumon wasps, use their ovipositor to insert eggs in other insects, called hosts. When the ichneumon larvae hatch they feed on the hosts' bodies, eventually causing death. In many parasitic wasps the ovipositor is very long and in some species it is strong enough to pierce plants and burrow through the tissues to reach hosts inside.

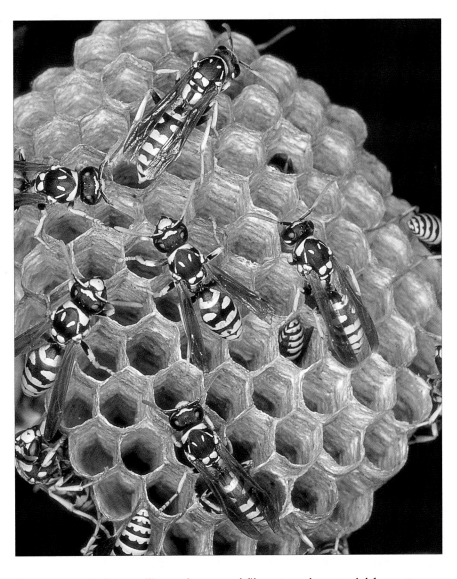

*Paper wasps,* Polistes gallicus, *chew wood fibers to make material for nests.*

Parasitic wasps live off a wide variety of plants as well as animals. Gall wasps, for example, lay their eggs in the buds, leaves and roots of plants and trees, particularly oak trees and rose bushes. Their larvae develop within structures of swollen plant tissue, known as galls, that offer a protected area of food cells for the larvae to feed on.

## Defense mechanisms
Stings are the most effective weapon of honeybees and are mostly used by female workers in defense of their nest. However, the sting can be used only once. A worker will disembowel herself by violently struggling to get free, leaving her barbed sting lodged firmly in the enemy. Although the bee dies as a result, muscles in a specialized venom gland continue to pump poison into the predator for up to one minute. Another gland attached to the sting simultaneously releases an alarm pheromone (chemical substance) that alerts other workers in the colony to the attack.

| CLASSIFICATION | |
|---|---|
| **CLASS** Insecta | |
| **ORDER** Hymenoptera | |
| **SUBORDER** Apocrita | |
| **NUMBER OF SPECIES** More than 120,000 | |

# Bees and Wasps Family Tree

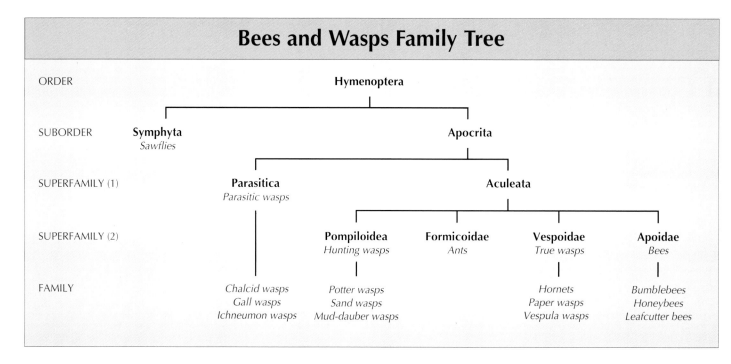

| ORDER | | | | Hymenoptera | | | |
|---|---|---|---|---|---|---|---|
| SUBORDER | **Symphyta**<br>*Sawflies* | | | | **Apocrita** | | |
| SUPERFAMILY (1) | | | **Parasitica**<br>*Parasitic wasps* | | | **Aculeata** | |
| SUPERFAMILY (2) | | | | **Pompiloidea**<br>*Hunting wasps* | **Formicoidae**<br>*Ants* | **Vespoidae**<br>*True wasps* | **Apoidae**<br>*Bees* |
| FAMILY | | Chalcid wasps<br>Gall wasps<br>Ichneumon wasps | | Potter wasps<br>Sand wasps<br>Mud-dauber wasps | | Hornets<br>Paper wasps<br>Vespula wasps | Bumblebees<br>Honeybees<br>Leafcutter bees |

The ability to sting predators is only one form of defense used by bees and wasps. They are often tough and distasteful items of prey. Birds and other predators learn to associate the coloration of the bee or wasp with a difficult or unpleasant item of food, leaving such prey alone in future. Many entirely harmless animals have taken advantage of this and have evolved an appearance that closely resembles the distasteful bees and wasps. This form of mimicry is found in butterflies and moths, for example the hornet moth, *Sesia apiformis*, and in true flies of the order Diptera, such as *Volucella bombylans*.

## Life cycle

Many of the true wasps are predators that hunt invertebrates. However, most bees collect pollen, nectar (a sweet liquid made by glands inside flowers) and other plant foods for themselves and their larvae. They have specialized hairs on the hind legs or the undersides of the abdomen for transporting pollen.

The nests of solitary bees and wasps are built by a single female working alone. In social species, a network of female workers carries out the construction of nests. Solitary bees and wasps are generally nonaggressive, whereas social bees and wasps are easily antagonized and may attack in large numbers if provoked.

Bee and wasp grubs, or larvae, lack legs and usually have a very small head. The larvae grow through a series of molts and, as in other advanced insects, eventually become pupae. During the pupal stage almost all of the larval tissues are broken down and reassembled into the adult bee or wasp. Pupae are normally held in some form of silky cocoon, but this structure may be flimsy.

When the adults emerge, they continue the life cycle by breeding and laying eggs. However, not all species have to mate in order to produce young. Many female Hymenoptera can produce young from both fertilized and unfertilized eggs.

*Like most bees, the hairy-legged mining bee,* Dasypoda hirtipes, *lives alone. Each female digs a burrow in the ground up to 2 feet (60 cm) deep in which she lays her eggs.*

## Great variety of nests

Bees and wasps build nests of all shapes and sizes. Many, including both solitary and social species, excavate nests in the ground, especially in areas with light, sandy soils. Underground nests usually consist of a tunnel and several side branches, ending in one or more food-stocked cells.

Some bees and wasps construct exposed nests above ground. Mason bees make nests of sand and soil glued together with their own saliva. Paper wasps of the genus *Polistes* tear strips of fiber from dead wood, chewing them to a pulp. They mold the pulp into hexagonal cells that give their nests a distinctive pattern. Other species use mud or chewed leaves as nest-building materials.

Nests provide a safe place in which eggs can develop and hatch and are stocked with a supply of food for the larvae. For example, female spider-hunting wasps in the family Pompilidae lay their eggs on the paralyzed bodies of spiders that they have placed in a simple burrow. Once they hatch the larval Pompilids devour the spiders. However, some nests are parasitized by other species of insect, even by other bees and wasps. Cuckoo wasps and cuckoo bees lay their eggs inside nests made by different species, and their larvae consume food laid down for the resident larvae. In a few cases, the parasitic larvae kill and eat the larvae of the host species.

## Queens, workers and drones

Although by far the largest number of bees and wasps are solitary, the Hymenoptera are famous for the social biology of some of their groups. Social bees choose secluded sites such as hollow trees and deep crevices in rocks for their nests. Social wasps build their nests in a variety of places, including under the eaves of houses, inside plant stems and rock crevices, suspended from tree branches and underground.

The honeybee is a well-known example of a social insect. In each honeybee hive there is a large female, or queen, which is the sole producer of offspring. There are also many nonreproducing workers that tend to the queen and her young. The queen herself never leaves the nest to seek sustenance.

Fertilized eggs result in females. Most females become workers, whereas a few that are fed a special food called royal jelly (containing sugars, proteins and vitamins) become queens and may establish new hives of their own. Unfertilized eggs, which are rare, give rise to male bees called drones, the only task of which is to mate with the queen. Having performed this act, the drones die or are killed by workers.

Queen honeybees lay an egg in each cell over a period of three or four years. After this time they become too old for further reproduction, and workers kill them. When new queens hatch, they are killed by the existing queen. However, if the existing queen is old, new queens are allowed to survive and may take over from their predecessor.

*Bee and wasp larvae (above) turn into adults during the pupal stage. The transformation occurs in a nest or within a silk cocoon suspended from plants.*

## Importance to humans

Bees often feed from flowers, the adults having mouthparts like drinking straws that are adapted for drinking nectar. Honeybees and bumblebees have very long tongues, allowing them to feed at long-necked flowers, while the bees of other groups have considerably shorter tongues. The collection of nectar in this way is important to humans because it is the raw material from which honey is made. Bees are also major pollinators, moving pollen from one flower to another and thereby fertilizing the receiving plant. This role is so important that hives of honeybees are often taken to orchards and other crops and left there to ensure that the fruit trees and crop plants are fertilized.

Wasps, too, are of vital importance to humans. Parasitic and predatory wasps that hunt other insects perform an essential role in keeping down numbers of pest species. This natural occurrence is of benefit to farmers, so much so that certain parasitic species are often deliberately released among crops to control pests. Parasitic wasps normally attack a particular insect or group of insects, leaving other species alone. The wasp *Encarsia formosa* offers a good example. It is introduced into greenhouses to control whitefly, a group of very damaging pests. The use of wasps in this way is known as biological pest control, and it greatly reduces the need for powerful insecticides that can harm the environment.

*For particular species see:*
- BUMBLEBEE• CHALCID WASP • GALL WASP
- HONEYBEE • HORNET • HUNTING WASP
- ICHNEUMON WASP • LEAFCUTTER BEE • PAPER WASP
- SAWFLY • VELVET ANT • VESPULA WASP

# BEETLES AND BUGS

*An adult tiger beetle,* Cicindela hybrida. *Beetles use strong mouthparts to slice into animals and plants and suck the juices.*

BEETLES AND BUGS ARE found in most habitats, including in lakes and rivers, on mountaintops, underground, inside buildings and within the living tissues of plants. The two groups of insects are often confused with each other but are quite distantly related. Beetles belong to the Coleoptera, the largest order in the animal kingdom. They include the heaviest of all insects, the hercules beetle, *Dynastes neptunus*, and the goliath beetle, *Goliathus giganteus*, which weigh 3½ ounces (100 g). At the other end of the size scale, many beetles are under 5 millimeters long. Bugs belong to the order Hemiptera, which is divided into two suborders, the Homoptera, including the cicadas, hoppers and aphids, and the Heteroptera, including the shieldbugs and plant bugs.

## Structural differences

There is a tremendous range of form within beetles and bugs. Like all insects, they have three main body segments: the head, the thorax, from which three pairs of jointed legs arise, and the abdomen. Most species have two pairs of wings, but some have a single pair and others are wingless.

Beetles have biting mouthparts, or mandibles, whereas bugs possess a piercing beak, the rostrum, which is used to suck juices from plants or other animals. The presence of the rostrum is the only obvious connection between bugs that belong to the Homoptera and those belonging to the Heteroptera. Members of the two bug suborders are otherwise quite different in appearance.

The wing structure of beetles and bugs differs in several respects. Beetles have a pair of tough and horny forewings, known as elytra, which usually cover the entire abdomen. The elytra meet neatly along the midline of the abdomen without overlap, giving beetles a characteristic armored appearance. An exception is the rove beetles (Staphylinidae), in which only part of the abdomen is covered by the elytra. The hind wings of beetles are membranous (thin and pliable) and held folded beneath the elytra when not in use.

Not all Homopteran bugs have wings, but those that do look quite different from beetles because their wings are all of uniform texture and are usually held roofwise over the body at rest. Heteropteran bugs are more likely to be confused with beetles. In this suborder the hind wings are always membranous, like those of beetles, and the forewings are largely horny or leathery. However, the forewings are clearly divided into two regions, with a membranous tip. All four wings are folded flat over the body at rest, the forewings meeting in such a way that the membranous areas of the wing-tips overlap to form a triangle.

## From egg to adult

Beetles and bugs have different methods of developing from egg to adult. Bugs, in common with grasshoppers, crickets, cockroaches and earwigs, undergo a gradual transformation known as incomplete metamorphosis, or hemimetabolous. The juvenile stages of bugs are called nymphs, and look like miniature versions of adults. Nymphs develop through a series of stages, referred to as molts and instars, each of

| CLASSIFICATION Beetles | |
|---|---|
| **PHYLUM** Arthropoda | |
| **CLASS** Insecta | |
| **ORDER** Coleoptera | |
| **NUMBER OF SPECIES** About 350,000 | |

| CLASSIFICATION Bugs | |
|---|---|
| **PHYLUM** Arthropoda | |
| **CLASS** Insecta | |
| **ORDER** Hemiptera | |
| **SUBORDER** Homoptera Heteroptera | |
| **NUMBER OF SPECIES** About 70,000 | |

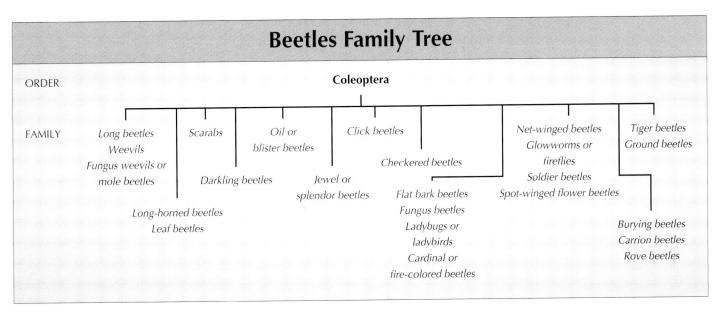

# Beetles Family Tree

| ORDER | Coleoptera |
|---|---|

| FAMILY | | | | | | | |
|---|---|---|---|---|---|---|---|

Long beetles
Weevils
Fungus weevils or
mole beetles

Scarabs

Oil or
blister beetles

Click beetles

Net-winged beetles
Glowworms or
fireflies

Tiger beetles
Ground beetles

Checkered beetles

Darkling beetles

Jewel or
splendor beetles

Soldier beetles
Spot-winged flower beetles

Long-horned beetles
Leaf beetles

Flat bark beetles
Fungus beetles
Ladybugs or
ladybirds
Cardinal or
fire-colored beetles

Burying beetles
Carrion beetles
Rove beetles

which is closer to the adult than the stage that came before. In winged species tiny wing-pads on the outside of the body grow with each molt until, after the final molt, the fully winged adult emerges. The nymphs and adults of each species of bug generally share the same food source.

Beetles, together with butterflies, bees and flies, develop into adults by complete metamorphosis, or holometabolous. The juvenile stages of beetles are called larvae. The larva that emerges from the egg is quite different in appearance from the adult into which it will eventually turn and does not necessarily feed on the same source of food. The larva progresses through a series of molts until it enters a stage called the pupa. Inside the pupa the process of metamorphosis occurs, in which cells comprising the larval structure are first broken down and then reassembled to form the adult beetle.

Bug nymphs always have legs, whereas beetle larvae often do not. However, the most important distinguishing feature between bug nymphs and beetle larvae is that the former always have a beaklike rostrum, the latter biting mouthparts.

## Food and feeding

Beetles and bugs exploit a huge range of foodstuffs. The proportion of herbivores is higher in bugs, with up to 90 percent of all species feeding on plant matter, compared to 30–40 percent in beetles.

Herbivorous beetles and bugs feed on the sap, bark, leaves, roots, flowers, pollen and seeds of plants and trees. They include many serious pests of gardens, agricultural

land and forestry plantations. Chief among them are the aphids (Aphididae), also known as greenfly and blackfly. These bugs feed by attacking phloem (the vascular tissue in plants that transports sugars and other nutrients), causing physical damage and transmitting viruses to plants.

Most beetles and bugs are not pests, however. Indeed, some actually reduce pest numbers. For example, ladybugs (Coccinellidae), which despite their name are beetles rather than bugs, specialize in hunting aphids. Many beetles and bugs play an important role in the ecosystems of which they are part. Dung beetles (Geotrupidae), for instance, are able to make use of animal dung by gathering it into balls as food reserves. Moreover, beetles and bugs are in themselves a major source of food for a wide variety of animals, including mammals, birds, fish, reptiles and amphibians.

*A freshly hatched beetle. The life history of a beetle starts with an egg, from which a larva hatches. The larva feeds and grows before entering a pupa, where it transforms into an adult.*

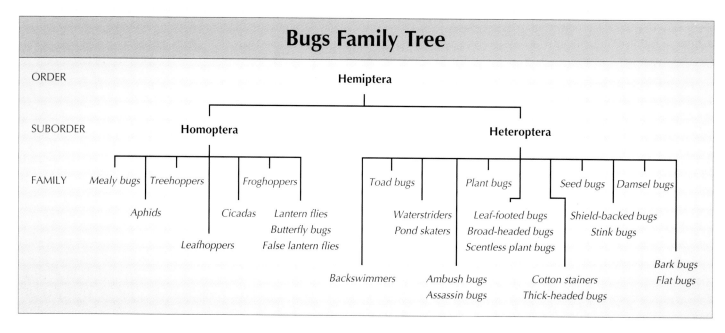

# Bugs Family Tree

| ORDER | Hemiptera | | | | | |
|---|---|---|---|---|---|---|

| SUBORDER | Homoptera | | | Heteroptera | | |
|---|---|---|---|---|---|---|

| FAMILY | Mealy bugs | Treehoppers | Froghoppers | Toad bugs | Plant bugs | Seed bugs | Damsel bugs |

Aphids     Cicadas    Lantern flies     Waterstriders    Leaf-footed bugs    Shield-backed bugs

Butterfly bugs     Pond skaters    Broad-headed bugs    Stink bugs

Leafhoppers     False lantern flies     Scentless plant bugs

Bark bugs

Backswimmers     Ambush bugs     Cotton stainers    Flat bugs

Assassin bugs     Thick-headed bugs

Although the great majority of bugs are herbivores, the suborder Heteroptera includes a variety of scavengers and predators. Among them are several families of aquatic bugs, such as the pond skaters (Gerridae) and backswimmers (Notonectidae), and certain plant bugs (Miridae) that specialize in stealing prey trapped in spiderwebs. Other predatory bugs include the ambush bugs (Phymatidae), which feed rather like a praying mantis, by seizing prey with their powerful legs, and the assassin bugs (Reduviidae). The bee assassin bug, *Apiomerus flaviventris*, injects a powerful, fast-acting toxin into its prey, the effect of which can be more painful to humans than bee and wasp stings. Some bugs, such as the bed bug, *Cimex lectularius*, suck blood from host animals, including cattle and humans.

Over half of all beetles are predators, scavengers, or both. The scavengers include the many burying beetles (Necrophorus), which feed on animal carcasses, and the tumblebug, *Canthon humectus*, which eats dung. Many long-horned beetle (Cerambycidae) larvae feed on wood inside tree trunks, whereas the adults feed solely on flower nectar and pollen. Some beetles are parasitic, such as the oil beetles (Meloidae), which during the larval stage live inside the bodies of other insects.

## Scientific study

The proliferation of beetles and bugs, coupled with their diverse appearance and habits, ensures their interest to naturalists. Also, the short

generation times and small size of these insects make them easy to rear in a laboratory. Much research into their behavior has been undertaken, although there is much still to learn.

*For particular species see:*
- APHID • BACKSWIMMER • BURYING BEETLE • CICADA
- CLICK BEETLE • COCKCHAFER • COLORADO BEETLE
- DIVING BEETLE • FIREFLY • GLOWWORM
- HOPPER • LADYBUG • LONG-HORNED BEETLE
- OIL BEETLE • POND SKATER • SCALE INSECT
- SCARAB BEETLE • SHIELDBUG • VINE PEST
- WATER BEETLE • WATER SCORPION • WEEVIL
- WHIRLIGIG BEETLE • WHITEFLY

*Most bugs are vegetarians, but assassin bugs are voracious predators with a powerful bite.*

# BEIRA ANTELOPE

*Photographs of beira antelope are few and far between. This male was photographed in captivity at a private collection.*

THE BEIRA ANTELOPE is lightly built, the males standing no more than 20 inches (51 cm) at the shoulder, the females being slightly larger. On the neck and back, the coat is a purplish-gray and finely grizzled, the extreme tips of the hairs being white. The underparts are light yellow and not so pale as in most antelope. There is white on only the axilla, or armpit, and groin. The outer forearms and thighs are yellowish-fawn, darkening lower down the limbs. The short, bushy tail is the same color as the back. The eyes are surrounded by white rings and the ears are large and leaf-shaped.

Only the male beira antelope has horns. These small, slightly curving structures are often almost hidden by the ears. They normally grow to 4–5 inches (10–13 cm), but the longest on record measured 5½ inches (14 cm).

## Elusive rock climber

In the heyday of big game–hunting in the latter half of the 19th century, there were reports of a small antelope that lived in the dry hills of the region then known as Somaliland. This creature was highly elusive and it was some time before hunters were able to get specimens of the antelope, which the Somalis called *behra* or *beira*. The beira antelope, as the species is now called, is still poorly known. It is very scarce and its elusiveness makes study difficult. For example, nothing is known of the beira antelope's breeding habits. Presumably, females give birth at the beginning of the rainy season, as do female antelopes of other species.

The beira antelope is confined to the hills and plateaus of northern Somalia and Ethiopia, where it lives among the stony outcrops and precipices. Its agility drew the attention of hunters, who found it difficult to get near this antelope that was able to bound around the rocks and up slopes like a mountain goat. The beira antelope's unusual hooves, which are short with flexible pads of cartilage underneath, help it obtain an excellent purchase on rocks, acting rather like rubber-soled shoes.

Herds of beira antelope tend to be small. There are usually six or seven antelope in each herd, although there may be as many as 12.

One or two will be bucks and the rest does. There is generally one herd living on each hill, which seems to form a clearly defined territory. Hunters have reported that when one antelope in a herd is shot the remaining animals run away but soon return to the same spot, and that the antelopes continue returning despite repeated disturbance. If such reports are reliable, the species is clearly vulnerable to hunting.

The beira antelope presumably browses any of the herbage that grows sparsely in its arid homeland. Dry grasses and the prickly leaves of dwarf mimosa, a type of shrub, are known to feature prominently in its diet. The hardy species also appears to go without water for extended periods, obtaining all it needs from succulents (plants with fleshy tissues that conserve water) and, perhaps, from dew.

## Hunters' contribution to science

Much of our early knowledge of animals found in remote parts of the world was based on the observations and specimens supplied by hunters. This was especially true of rarer species. Indeed, our understanding of the beira antelope has advanced very little since this species was first discovered by European explorers at the end of the 19th century.

In 1885 Captain H. G. C. Swayne, who had explored the Somali hills, wrote of a "small, red antelope" with the "habits of a klipspringer," but which the Somalis knew to be of a different kind. Swayne and several other European hunters were unable to get a shot at the antelopes. The animals were too small, wary, agile and quick, and superbly camouflaged in their rocky surroundings. Eventually, Swayne offered a handsome reward and managed to buy the heads of a male and female antelope from some local people. He passed the specimens to the Zoological Society of London, which duly described the species and named it *Dorcatragus*, meaning goat-antelope.

## Uncertain future

There was estimated to be a population of about 1,000 beira antelopes in Somaliland in 1905. It is unclear whether this figure has since changed because the antelopes' shy nature and barren, inaccessible habitat make it difficult to carry out serious scientific studies. Moreover, in recent years there have been several armed conflicts in the Horn of Africa and the region's political situation remains highly unstable.

Today, most conservationists consider the beira antelope to be threatened by uncontrolled hunting, habitat degradation and competition for food with feral goats. This state of affairs is made worse by the lack of a captive population of beira

---

## BEIRA ANTELOPE

| | |
|---|---|
| CLASS | **Mammalia** |
| ORDER | **Artiodactyla** |
| FAMILY | **Bovidae** |
| GENUS AND SPECIES | ***Dorcatragus megalotis*** |

WEIGHT
**20–24 lb. (9–11 kg)**

LENGTH
**Head and body: 30–33 in. (75–85 cm); shoulder height: 20–30 in. (50–75 cm); tail: 20–30 in. (50–75 cm)**

DISTINCTIVE FEATURES
**Short body; long legs; large ears with white internal hairs**

DIET
**Coarse grasses and mimosa leaves**

BREEDING
**Breeding season: only births recorded in April; gestation period: estimated to be about 180 days**

LIFE SPAN
**Not known**

HABITAT
**Stony hills and hot, arid plateaus**

DISTRIBUTION
**Northern Somalia, Djibouti and adjacent parts of Ethiopia**

STATUS
**Vulnerable. Small population in Somalia and Ethiopia; probably near-extinct in Djibouti.**

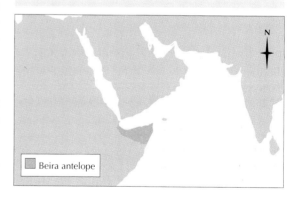

Beira antelope

---

antelopes in North American or European zoos, which would allow the species to survive should the wild population become extinct. However, a few of the species are held in at least one private collection of antelopes, and it may be possible to use these animals as the basis for a captive breeding program in the future.

# BELLBIRD

The bellbirds are named after their fantastic, ringing voices, which have a metallic quality. There are six species. In the forests of South America are four jay-sized species related to the cotingas: the white, bearded, bare-throated and three-wattled bellbirds. All four belong to the genus *Procnias*. The three-wattled bellbird, *P. tricarunculata*, is an odd-looking bird with white on the head, neck and shoulders and three grayish black, turkeylike wattles dangling from the base of the bill. A fifth species, the New Zealand bellbird, *Anthornis melanura*, belongs to the honeyeater family. It is also a forest-dweller, and when several sing in chorus they sound like tinkling bells. The remaining species is the crested bellbird, *Oreoica gutturalis*, of Australia. It is a member of yet another family, the whistlers, and is the species treated here.

The crested bellbird is related to the flycatchers, and is a little larger than a thrush. It is a highly distinctive bird, gray-brown above and whitish below, with a crest of grayish-black feathers and, in the male, a black breast patch. The female is more somber than the male, the underparts being plainer and the crest less obvious. At close range the striking reddish or orange eye can be seen.

## Singing ventriloquist
The crested bellbird lives in the arid interior of Australia, among rocks, scrub, acacia bush and eucalyptus woodland, where it is found singly or in pairs. A common species in most areas, it becomes relatively scarce in coastal regions that experience higher rainfall.

Relatively little is known of the crested bellbird's habits because the species tends to hide in cover and is more often heard than seen. It spends much time on the ground, where it is unobtrusive and easy to overlook, although it flies up into trees when disturbed. However, the song of the crested bellbird is very familiar. This begins as a rapid succession of notes, or a pair of notes repeated together more slowly, then repeated three times more quickly, the last note being remarkably bell-like.

Even when a bellbird is singing, it can prove difficult to locate because its voice has such a markedly ventriloquial quality. The first notes are low, and sound as if they are coming from a distance. As the volume rises, the bird seems to be flying nearer until the final resonant note seems to be uttered overhead. Yet all the time the bellbird has been singing from a fixed point in a tree only a few yards away. Observations of

singing birds suggest that they turn their heads this way and that, and this may explain the ventriloquial qualities of their song.

Travelers in Australia sometimes confused the bellbird's song with the noise made by the bells on their horses' necks, which made it difficult to find any horses that had wandered while grazing at night. Aborigines traditionally considered that the song foretold bad luck.

## Hoarding food
Crested bellbirds search the ground for large insects and seeds. Caterpillars in particular are stored in their nests during the breeding season.

*The male crested bellbird's territorial song is one of the most unusual sounds of spring in Australia.*

191

Food hoarding of this kind is well known among mammals but is rare among birds. Foods stored by birds are normally fruits of some kind, such as nuts and berries, or animal carcasses, such as the dead insects, lizards and small birds that shrikes impale on thorns. What makes crested bellbirds unusual is that they store live prey. A pair of bellbirds may store up to 20 caterpillars, either decorating the rim of the nest with them or simply dropping the insects inside among the clutch of eggs.

## Living larders

To prevent the caterpillars from crawling away the adult bellbirds firmly pinch the victims with their bills. This paralyzes the nervous system of the caterpillars, which can breathe and wriggle but are unable to move in a coordinated fashion. The bellbird hoard is therefore a supply of fresh meat that will not deteriorate. It recalls the European mole's habit of nipping off the heads of earthworms and then storing them underground as a living larder.

The immobilized caterpillars are used to feed the chicks. It has been suggested that the store is an emergency supply for use in dry spells. In parched conditions caterpillars and beetles dig down into the ground to where the soil is moist, and where bellbirds cannot find them.

## Secluded nest-site

The song of the crested bellbird can be heard throughout the year but reaches a climax in spring, August to December, when the species breeds. It is uttered by males in possession of a territory. The tone and phrasing of the song vary markedly between different males and from one district to another.

The crested bellbird's nest is a deep cup of leaves and pieces of bark, lined with dried grass and rootlets. It is usually well hidden in a hollow stump or low down among suckers of the thick foliage. Sometimes a pair of bellbirds builds a nest under strips of dead bark hanging from a tree trunk. Three or four bluish white eggs blotched with dark green or black are laid. The female is responsible for most of the incubation but both sexes feed the chicks.

## What's in a name?

Quite often birds and mammals have been given names suggested by their song or call, especially if the sound is rhythmically repeated. The most obvious example is the cuckoo, *Cuculus canorus*, a common parasitic bird of Europe and Asia. The black-legged kittiwake, *Rissa tridactyla*, and the hoopoe, *Upapa epops*, are other Old World birds with onomatopoeic names, or names formed in imitation of a sound. The Aborigine peoples

### CRESTED BELLBIRD

| | |
|---|---|
| CLASS | **Aves** |
| ORDER | **Passeriformes** |
| FAMILY | **Pachycephalidae** |
| GENUS AND SPECIES | ***Oreoica gutturalis*** |

ALTERNATIVE NAMES
**Pan-pan-panella; Dick-Dick, the devil (archaic)**

LENGTH
**Head to tail: 8–9 in. (20–23 cm)**

DISTINCTIVE FEATURES
**Gray and black crest. Male: prominent white area on forehead and throat, bordered by black band. Female: browner and plainer.**

DIET
**Caterpillars, insect grubs, beetles and other invertebrates; some seeds**

BREEDING
**Age at first breeding: 1 year; breeding season: August–December, or after rain; number of eggs: 3 or 4; incubation period: not known; fledging period: not known; breeding interval: 1 year**

LIFE SPAN
**Not known**

HABITAT
**Arid scrub and eucalyptus woodland**

DISTRIBUTION
**Australia, except for some coastal areas**

STATUS
**Generally common**

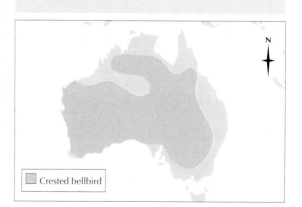

Crested bellbird

native to Australia have several onomatopoeic names for the crested bellbird, among them *pan-pan-panella*, and the first European settlers gave it such colorful names as *Dick-Dick, the devil* and *tip-top, top o' the wattle*, phrases that resemble the bird's song.

# BELUGA WHALE

THE NAME "BELUGA" refers to two unrelated animals. One is a fish, the Russian sturgeon, which is discussed in a separate article, and the other is the beluga, or white, whale.

The beluga whale is a member of the dolphin and porpoise family, in which it forms a distinct group with the narwhal. Like the narwhal, it has a rounded head and lacks a dorsal fin. Adult belugas can be distinguished from all other whales by their white skin. When young, their skin is gray, but this becomes white when they are about 4 years old due to a steady reduction of the black pigment melanin. Some beluga whales pass through a mottled brown phase before becoming white.

The largest beluga whale on record was 18 feet (5.5 m) long. Average-sized individuals reach 10–14 feet (3–4 m), and males are about 1 foot (30 cm) longer than females. Beluga whales are slow swimmers, cruising at 5 miles per hour (8 km/h) and making 9 miles per hour (14 km/h) when in a hurry. By way of comparison, large rorqual whales (the large species in the Balaenopteridae) swim at 23 miles per hour (37 km/h) during sprints lasting 10–15 minutes, and dolphins keep up with ships traveling at 26–28 miles per hour (42–45 km/h).

## Singing schools of the Arctic

Beluga whales live in Arctic seas where the pack ice has broken up. Sometimes they become hemmed into pools by the freezing of the sea. They may be able to crack the ice by ramming it with their padded heads, but if it freezes solid they cannot surface to breathe, and so perish. In severe winters the whales move south and have, on rare occasions, been recorded in Scotland, Ireland, the Baltic Sea and Japan.

Beluga whales frequent coasts, occasionally swimming up rivers. In 1863 one was caught 700 miles (1,125 km) up the Yukon River in western Canada. Normally the whales stay within the Arctic Circle in the European sector of the Arctic, moving no further south than Newfoundland in the western Atlantic, or Vancouver Island and Kamchatka in the Pacific.

At one time schools of beluga whales used to be up to 10,000 strong, but intensive whaling during the 19th century has severely reduced their numbers. Normally the whales form small

herds of about a dozen, although they sometimes still gather in thousands around river mouths during the summer months.

British whalers used to call the beluga whale the sea canary because the sounds it makes can be heard above water, and resemble the song of a bird. The beluga whale also growls and roars, and in Russia someone noisy is said to "squeal like a beluga." These noises are accompanied by a rush of air bubbles from the blowhole, or nostril, on top of the head, so the beluga can be said to be whistling through its nose.

## Seabed feeders

Beluga whales are members of the group of toothed whales, or Odontoceti, to which the sperm whales and dolphins also belong. They have 32 to 40 teeth with which they catch a range of marine organisms, swallowing them without

*Beluga whales produce a chorus of strange noises, probably to help the members of a school stay in touch.*

## BELUGA WHALE

| | |
|---|---|
| CLASS | **Mammalia** |
| ORDER | **Cetacea** |
| FAMILY | **Monodontidae** |
| GENUS AND SPECIES | ***Delphinapterus leucas*** |

ALTERNATIVE NAMES
**Belukha; white whale; sea canary (archaic)**

LENGTH
**Usually 10–16½ ft. (3–5 m), exceptionally up to 18 ft. (5.5 m)**

DISTINCTIVE FEATURES
**All-white body, grayish in young; bulbous forehead; lacks dorsal fin**

DIET
**Fish, cuttlefish, squid and crustaceans, especially shrimps and crabs**

BREEDING
**Age at first breeding: 5–10 years; breeding season: late February–May; gestation period: probably about 420 days; number of young: 1; breeding interval: usually about 3 years**

LIFE SPAN
**Up to 25 years in captivity**

HABITAT
**Shallow coastal waters and lower reaches of large rivers**

DISTRIBUTION
**Circumpolar range includes Arctic and subarctic seas**

STATUS
**Population: 50,000 to 70,000**

*Inshore waters rich in marine life are the main feeding grounds of beluga whales.*

chewing. Their varied diet includes shrimps, crabs, cuttlefish and fish, especially halibut, flounder and Arctic char. Hunting takes place mainly on the seabed in shallow coastal waters. Most whales have weak ribs that cannot support their body weight, and stranding on a shore is almost always fatal because the lungs become compressed, causing the whale to suffocate. Beluga whales, however, are more resistant to suffocation. They often swim into shallow water where they can hardly float, and where other whales would become stranded.

Female beluga whales give birth to a single calf, measuring 5 feet (1.5 m), about 14 months after mating. The calf is nursed for 8 months. Instead of the calf sucking at a teat as in terrestrial mammals, the milk glands contract and squirt milk into its mouth.

## New threats

Beluga whales are hunted by polar bears but their main natural enemies are killer whales. The latter can tackle full-grown belugas, although they prefer to hunt the young. There are reports of beluga whales becoming noticeably distressed merely at the sight of killer whales.

One of the biggest threats now facing the species is chemical contaminants in the ocean, which cause cancers and fetal abnormalities.

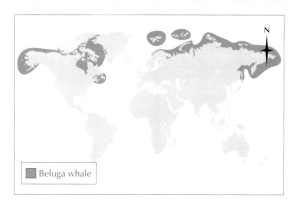

Beluga whale

Beluga whales living in St. Lawrence Sound, Canada, may accumulate such high levels of contaminants in their bodies that they are treated as toxic waste when they die. Oil exploration and hydroelectric plants also cause disturbance to beluga whale populations.

# BICHIR

A FAMILY OF FRESHWATER FISH over 2 feet (60 cm) long, bichirs are the descendants of a large group of extinct fish. They have many primitive characteristics and are related to the sturgeons, which are also primitive fish. Fossils of bichirs have been found in North Africa, but bichirs now occur only in the watersheds of the Nile and Congo rivers. There are nine related species similar in size to one another and all found in tropical Africa.

A bichir has a long body, a small but broad head and a rounded tail, but its distinctive feature is a series of "finlets" along its back, which may be raised or lowered. Each finlet is flaglike and consists of a single stiff ray to which a fringe of one or several fin-rays is attached. The pectoral fins, too, are peculiar. They are fanlike, almost as if stalked. The body is covered with an armor of hard, rhombic scales, made of the hard protein, ganoin.

Bichirs are green or yellow-brown in color, sometimes mottled and with darker spots or stripes. An exception is the ornate bichir, *Polypterus ornatipinnis,* of the middle and upper reaches of the Congo River, which has a dark blackish body with white spots.

## Air-breathing fish

Bichirs live hidden among the thickets of large water plants at the margins of rivers and lakes, from which they come out at night to feed. Their diet consists of small aquatic animals, mainly insect larvae and small worms, but also small frogs and fish. Bichirs have gills in addition to a lunglike swim bladder, yet if denied air for even a short time they die.

To breathe air, a bichir swims slowly to the surface, takes a quick gulp and quickly swims down to the bottom. In most fish, even those that gulp air, the swim bladder is single. In the bichirs it is paired, like the lungs of a terrestrial vertebrate, although the two parts are of unequal size.

## Prowling hunters

A peculiar feature of bichir behavior is the use of the pectoral fins almost as legs, to support the front part of the body. A bichir may rest at the bottom, supporting itself on these fins, with the head raised, rather in the manner of a quadruped on land, such as a lizard. When hunting for food, it behaves quite unlike other fish. It prowls, moving slowly forward inch by inch, pausing, raising the head as if sniffing around and then

*The bichir is a fish with many primitive features. It has gills, but must frequently come to the surface to gulp air.*

moving forward again. The unusual tubular nostrils, coupled with the small eyes, suggest that smell is used to locate food.

The almost catlike prowl is seen also when a bichir is confronted with any new object. It moves forward much in the manner of a cat stalking a mouse, but its pectoral fins are fluttering and the finlets on its back are raised, ready to swim backward if need arises. When moving quickly, the finlets are laid back, the pectoral fins are pressed close to the body and the bichir "drives" itself through the water with side-to-side, rather eel-like movements of the body.

## Leaping courtship

Spawning usually takes place in August and September, at the time of rains and associated floods, when rivers and lakes overflow to form marshes and swamps. Bichirs move out into these seasonal wetlands. Courtship begins with two bichirs leaping out of the water, after which they chase one another, keeping close together. After a while the pursuit is broken off.

There follows a brief rest, which is ended by the male going over to the female and nudging her with his head or brushing her with his anal fin, which is said to be swollen and folded at the breeding season. Practically nothing is known of the spawning itself until the larval stage. The larvae have an adhesive gland on the top of the head with which they cling to aquatic vegetation, and have a pair of external feathery gills, like those of newt larvae.

## Unusual anatomy

Bichirs have been described as among the most interesting fish of all for anatomical and evolutionary studies. Fish are divided into two major groups: the true, or bony, fish and the sharks, or cartilaginous fish. A bichir's skeleton is bony, and yet contains more than the usual amount of cartilage. Its intestine has a spiral valve, one of the hallmarks of sharks. Bichirs also have spiracles, openings behind each eye like an extra gill, which are another feature of many cartilaginous fish, and their hard, enamel-like, ganoid scales are similar to those of sharks. In their anatomy, therefore, bichirs have features typical of both cartilaginous fish and true fish.

## Missing links

Bichirs occupy a niche that may have been similar to that of the forebears of terrestrial vertebrates. In their lungs and limblike pectoral fins and in certain features of their behavior, bichirs seem to indicate the evolutionary line along which a land-living amphibian, probably a form of primitive salamander or newt, arose from an air-breathing fish able to use its paired fins as

## BICHIRS

| | |
|---|---|
| CLASS | **Osteichthyes** |
| SUBCLASS | **Actinopterygii** |
| ORDER | **Polypteriformes** |
| FAMILY | **Polypteridae** |
| GENUS | ***Polypterus*** |
| SPECIES | **9, including *P. bichir*** |

LENGTH
**Approximately 27½ in. (70 cm)**

DISTINCTIVE FEATURES
**Dorsal fin comprised of several flaglike "finlets;" hard, shiny scales cover head and body**

DIET
**Aquatic invertebrates, fish and amphibians, especially small frogs**

BREEDING
**Very poorly known. Breeding season: during rains and floods.**

LIFE SPAN
**Not known**

HABITAT
**Margins of freshwater rivers and lakes with dense aquatic vegetation**

DISTRIBUTION
**West and Central Africa: Lake Chad and watersheds of Nile and Congo Rivers**

STATUS
**Not known**

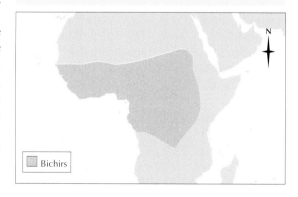

Bichirs

limbs. This theory corresponds perfectly with the fact that bichirs breed in marshes and swamps where the water contains little oxygen, and where fish that can breathe air are at an advantage. It may be that one of the ancestors of the bichir family took the evolutionary line that was to lead to the first amphibian, later the first reptile, and through it to the mammals and birds.

# BIG-HEADED TURTLE

*The big-headed turtle cannot tuck its head inside its shell. It relies on camouflage and a thick armor of modified scales for protection.*

THE BIG-HEADED TURTLE is the sole member of the family Platysternidae, and is one of the most remarkable turtles alive. It is unlike other freshwater turtles in many ways. The head is very large relative to the size of the body and cannot be withdrawn into the flat, broad shell. Instead, the head is heavily armored with horny plates on all sides. The turtle's jaws are powerful, the upper jaw ending in a curved beak, which is probably used to crack the shells of water snails. The tail is almost as long as the shell and covered with large scales. The short, strong legs are also covered with unusually large scales.

Male and female big-headed turtles are very similar, females having a slightly longer tail and a narrower head. Adults are olive, brownish or gray green, with black soft parts. Juveniles are more brightly colored.

## Nocturnal turtle

The big-headed turtle lives in Southeast Asia in mountain streams at altitudes of 6,000 feet (1,800 m) or more, where the temperature of the water seldom exceeds 59° F (15° C). Essentially aquatic and nocturnal, the turtle leaves water mainly to lay its eggs. However, it sometimes feeds on land and occasionally sunbathes during the day. Several writers have testified to the turtle's ability to climb. It probably does this with its strong claws and with the long tail being used, woodpecker-like, to support the body.

Not only does the adult big-headed turtle have rather dull coloration, but its shell usually becomes overgrown with algae, helping it blend in with its surroundings. Moreover, the turtle's flattened shell enables it quickly to take cover under stones and inside crevices, from which it can be removed only with difficulty. As a last

| BIG-HEADED TURTLE | |
|---|---|
| CLASS | **Reptilia** |
| ORDER | **Testudines** |
| FAMILY | **Platysternidae** |
| GENUS AND SPECIES | ***Platysternon megacephalum*** |

LENGTH
**Head to tail: up to 14 in. (35 cm); shell length: up to 7 in. (18 cm)**

DISTINCTIVE FEATURES
**Very large head that cannot be withdrawn into shell; large scales on head, legs and tail**

DIET
**Known to be predatory; probably feeds mainly on aquatic snails**

BREEDING
**Poorly known. Number of eggs: 1 or 2 per clutch.**

LIFE SPAN
**Not known**

HABITAT
**Clear, swift-flowing mountain streams above 6,000 ft. (1,800 m)**

DISTRIBUTION
**Thailand, Cambodia, Vietnam, southern China, Laos and Myanmar (Burma)**

STATUS
**May be vulnerable**

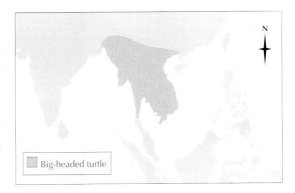

Big-headed turtle

resort the big-headed turtle also has an aggressive threat display unusual in turtles. With its mouth agape and the third eyelid, or nictitating membrane, drawn up over the eye to create a menacing appearance, the turtle hisses and snorts at its attacker.

# BIGHORN SHEEP

*Bighorn sheep are adapted to survive on scanty, poor-quality vegetation in uplands and dry country.*

THERE ARE SIX SPECIES of wild sheep, two of which are found in the New World: *Ovis canadensis*, the bighorn sheep of western North America, and *O. dalli*, the Dall sheep of Alaska and northwestern Canada. Of the other species, *O. ammon*, the argali or Marco Polo sheep, and *O. orientalis*, the urial or shapu, live in the former Soviet Union and southwestern Asia, while *O. laristan* is confined to Iran and *O. musimon*, the mouflon, occurs in Sardinia and Corsica. It is presumed that one or more of the four Old World species gave rise to the domestic sheep.

## Differences from goats

None of the wild sheep have woolly coats comparable to the domestic sheep. Rather, they have coats of coarse hair ranging in color from creamy-white to brown. The coat of the wild sheep is therefore not unlike that of a goat. However, sheep have characteristically narrow noses and concave foreheads, whereas goats have convex foreheads. Further differences are that sheep do not have the scent glands at the base of the tail nor a beard, although some male sheep have a fringe of long hair down the front of their necks.

There are also differences in the horns. Male bighorn sheep have massive horns curving around the back of the head past the neck, and in old animals coming forward to the level of the eye. The females have only small, slightly curving horns a few inches long. The horns are divided into concentric rings. Less obvious growth rings subdivide these into irregular segments. Each segment represents a year's growth, making it relatively straightforward to determine a bighorn sheep's age.

## Hardy animals

Bighorn sheep are found in many parts of the Rocky Mountains, in the states of New Mexico, Colorado and Nebraska and east to North Dakota. In Canada they occur in British Columbia, Alberta and Saskatchewan. The sheep live mainly in mountain pastures above the tree-line, reaching the most precipitous and inaccessible areas, but also occur in prairies and dry upland country. To the south, bighorn sheep are also found in the deserts of the southwestern United States and northern Mexico. These sheep belong to a different subspecies, often called the desert, or Mexican, bighorn.

The bighorns' diet consists largely of sedges and grasses, supplemented with a wide range of other plant food. In spring the sheep browse fresh aspen and spruce buds and dig up leguminous roots (the roots of plants belonging to the legume, or pea, family). During the fall and winter they also eat herbs, leaves, fungi, lichens and berries. In arid regions with sparse vegetation the sheep may have to browse cacti.

Bighorn sheep feed mainly during the day, especially in winter, but in summer will lie up during the heat of the day, finding resting places that give a full view of the surrounding area. Full-grown, healthy bighorn sheep have little to fear from anything except humans. However, lambs and old or sick individuals may fall prey to coyotes, pumas and eagles.

# BIGHORN SHEEP

| | |
|---|---|
| CLASS | **Mammalia** |
| ORDER | **Artiodactyla** |
| FAMILY | **Bovidae** |
| GENUS AND SPECIES | ***Ovis canadensis*** |

ALTERNATIVE NAMES
**O. c. californiana: Rocky Mountain bighorn, rimrock bighorn; O. c. mexicana: Mexican bighorn, desert bighorn; O. c. weemsi: Weems' bighorn; O. c. nelsoni: Nelson's bighorn**

LENGTH
**Head and body: 5½–6 ft. (1.6–1.8 m); shoulder height: 2¾–3¼ ft. (0.9–1 m)**

DISTINCTIVE FEATURES
**Massive, curled horns, smaller in female; stocky body**

DIET
**Grasses, sedges, roots, buds and leaves**

BREEDING
**Age at first breeding: usually 7 years (male), 2–3 years (female); breeding season: fall and early winter; gestation period: 150–180 days; number of young: 1 or 2; breeding interval: usually 1 year**

LIFE SPAN
**Up to 20 years**

HABITAT
**Alpine pastures, prairies and arid country, including rocky foothills and deserts**

DISTRIBUTION
**Throughout Rocky Mountains and in arid regions of southwestern U.S. and northernmost Mexico**

STATUS
**Critically endangered: Weems' bighorn; vulnerable: Mexican bighorn; lower risk: Rocky Mountain bighorn, Nelson's bighorn**

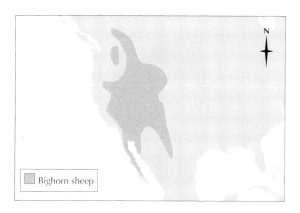
Bighorn sheep

## Social organization

Bighorn sheep live in small flocks outside the breeding season. In summer they form single-sex flocks of about a dozen sheep each. The groups of ewes, with their young, are usually largest. From October onward throughout the winter, mating takes place, and there is vigorous rivalry between the rams. Flocks tend to be mixed at this time because young rams are often forced to seek refuge among the ewes from the aggressive intolerance of the older rams.

Male bighorn sheep are physically capable of fertilizing females when 4 years old, but are rarely strong and dominant enough to breed until 7 years of age. Their necks become thicker and during the mating season they lose much of their fear of humans. At this age they join groups of males in which there is a strict dominance hierarchy. The ram with the largest horns is the leader. During November and early December, jousting takes place, not only between rams but also between ewes.

If an encounter comes to blows, the combatants may fight with their forelegs, kicking and pawing at one another, before indulging in spectacular, bone-jarring tournaments. The two contestants turn away from one another and, having retreated some distance, turn back and charge. The last few yards may be covered on hind legs alone, and just before the collision, heads are lowered and the full force of two bodies weighing 315 pounds (145 kg) each is taken on the foreheads. The impact is terrific and the contestants are frequently dazed, standing nose to nose, eyes glazed for half a minute. They back away and repeat the course. These combats may go on for hours with no decisive result, the contestants wandering away from each other.

*Male bighorn sheep fight for the right to mate with females. Success carries a high price: the bouts are so violent that dominant rams that have fought many times are likely to die young.*

Mating behavior reaches a peak in the second half of November. The rams move from one flock of ewes to another, singling out ewes and chasing them. If a ewe is receptive, she runs only a few yards before stopping and allowing a ram to mount her, otherwise a headlong chase takes place, with the ewe being chased by up to a dozen rams. Eventually she may find a crevice or rocky overhang in which to shelter and rest, but when she emerges the pursuit starts again.

## Lambing

Ewes prefer to mate with males with large horns. When a ewe is receptive, copulation takes only a few seconds but may occur several times. Later the ewe will mate with other rams. Ewes become mature at about 30 months, bearing their first lamb when 3 years old.

Just before the lambs are due, in May, the ewes retreat to the remotest parts of the mountains. Each ewe finds her own spot among rocky outcrops, preferably with a warm southerly exposure, in which to have her lamb. Unlike the fawns of deer, the newborn lambs are not left hidden while the mothers feed, but follow their mothers all the time.

When the lambs are strong enough, they are led down to the grassy slopes where the ewes and young assemble in flocks of 60 or more. In these maternal groups a lamb is sometimes looked after by a relative of their mother, generally a sister or half-sister, which seems to keep an watchful eye on it.

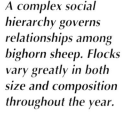

*A complex social hierarchy governs relationships among bighorn sheep. Flocks vary greatly in both size and composition throughout the year.*

## Status symbols

The horns of sheep, like the antlers of deer, serve as weapons. However, they are poorly suited to stabbing or battering opponents. The bighorn sheep's horns sprout from the top of the head then curve away around the neck, well out of the way of any impact. Moreover, the larger the horns grow, the less efficient they will be as weapons because they are more likely to snap off. In fights against predators the bighorn sheep instead kicks with its hard hooves, while the ritual fighting of courtship consists of head-to-head collisions, the bones of the forehead being built to reduce the effects of the concussion.

Some observations suggest that horns act as a badge of rank. When two rams meet they tilt their heads slightly, so presenting the other with a good view of the horns. If there is a significant difference in the size of the horns, the ram with the smaller ones, hence the younger and junior, will retreat, acknowledging the superiority of the other. Fighting breaks out only when rams with approximately equal-sized horns meet.

This argument cannot be the sole explanation of fighting between rival bighorn sheep, because there are sometimes fights involving several sheep at once. Up to 12 rams may take part in these free-for-all fights, which may go on all day with individuals retiring while they recuperate. It may be that there is a small amount of fighting to establish rank in the flock throughout the year, which flares up into a general mêlée in the excitement of the breeding season.

# BINTURONG

THE BINTURONG is a carnivore related to the palm civets and at first glance looks like a large, shaggy mongoose. It has a long coat with longer tail hair than body hair and large tufts that sprout from the back of its ears. The fur is black sprinkled with brown or gray on the tips of the hairs. The long whiskers, the ear tufts, and sometimes the face, are white. The tail is a little shorter than the head and body and is partially prehensile. Only one other carnivore has a prehensile tail: the kinkajou, *Potos flavus*.

The single species of binturong is found in Burma, Vietnam, Thailand, Malaysia and Indonesia and possibly in Assam, Nepal and Bhutan. It has also been recorded from southern Yunnan in China. Some zoologists recognize two races, the more northerly having a thicker winter coat.

## Treetop hunters

Although most writers describe the ease with which binturongs can be tamed, and in particular how they become affectionate and follow their owners like domestic dogs, only a little is known of their habits and breeding behavior. This is mainly due to their living in the treetops of dense jungles, or occasionally in the secondary forests that spring up after the jungle has been destroyed. Binturongs are nowhere common and, being nocturnal as well as arboreal, are often not known even to people living in the jungle. In some areas their fur is used to make caps and vests.

Despite the reported tameness, binturongs can be aggressive when cornered. If provoked sufficiently, they have a very powerful bite, capable, it is said, of severing fingers. Otherwise they challenge an aggressor with a low growl followed by an explosive spit and violent movements of the body. With the long coat bristling, this alone could well put a predator to flight.

During the day binturongs lie up in the forest canopy, often curling up with their heads tucked under their tails. Their eyes contract, like those of cats, to a vertical slit during the day. When binturongs descend to the ground, they hop awkwardly, but in the trees they are excellent climbers, although their movements are usually slow and deliberate and they have never

been seen to leap from one branch to another. They are strong and agile enough to walk upside down hanging from branches.

There is some doubt whether binturongs can support their entire weight with their tail. Certainly a young binturong can, but an adult uses its tail more as a brake, wrapping it around a branch as climbs down, then holding it against the trunk to slow itself. In this way the binturong uses its tail as an extra limb to steady itself.

## Unusually varied diet

Binturongs consume far more plant food than is usual for carnivores. They eat a large amount of fruit, invading plantations and orchards and stealing fruit from houses. Bananas are eaten by

*Binturongs are active mainly at night, when they emerge in search of food. Unlike most carnivores, much of their diet consists of fruits and plant shoots.*

201

squeezing the fruit out of the skin, which is discarded. Binturongs do hunt prey, however. They stalk roosting birds and small mammals, striking with unexpected speed. There are even records of binturongs diving for fish.

"Show me your teeth and I will tell you what you are," said the great French anatomist Baron Georges Cuvier, referring to an important principle of the classification of mammals. The carnivores, or flesh-eaters, generally have slicing teeth and insectivores, or insect-eaters, have pointed teeth for crunching their hard-bodied prey. However, there are no hard and fast rules in zoology and it is always possible to find exceptions. It was the realization that some carnivores do not eat meat alone, but include some vegetable matter in their diet, that enabled zoos to breed such animals successfully.

The binturong has the teeth of a typical carnivore, but a close examination of its skull shows that they are not designed for cutting up flesh. They have lost their cutting edges and are smaller and more rounded than is usual in carnivores. This pattern is more suitable for chewing and pulping fruit.

### Breeding in zoos

Virtually nothing is known of the breeding habits of binturongs in the wild. The young are apparently born in a cavity in a tree trunk, or in a cave. Binturongs have, however, bred quite often in zoos, where births have been recorded in March, July and November. Females drive males out of the nest box but are more tolerant of their mates than is the case with the females of other species. Two, or sometimes three, young are born. They huddle together on the bare floor of the nest box, which is kept scrupulously clean by the mother. They are weaned at 8 weeks, coming out of the nest box when ten weeks old, making snuffling noises that help the parents keep in touch with them.

*During the day binturongs rest up in the treetops. They sometimes venture into the open to sun themselves in a branch fork.*

## BINTURONG

| | |
|---|---|
| CLASS | **Mammalia** |
| ORDER | **Carnivora** |
| FAMILY | **Viverridae** |
| GENUS AND SPECIES | ***Arctictis binturong*** |

WEIGHT
**20–30 lb. (9–14 kg)**

LENGTH
**Head and body: 24–38 in. (61–96 cm); tail: 22–35 in. (56–89 cm)**

DISTINCTIVE FEATURES
**Long, shaggy coat; long, white whiskers; prehensile tail; relatively small, blunt teeth**

DIET
**Mainly fruits, leaves and carrion; sometimes birds and small mammals; rarely fish**

BREEDING
**Age at first breeding: 28–30 months; breeding season: all year; number of young: usually 2; gestation period: 84–99 days; breeding interval: 2 litters per year**

LIFE SPAN
**Up to 23 years in captivity**

HABITAT
**Dense tropical forest**

DISTRIBUTION
**Myanmar (Burma) to the Malay Peninsula, and on Sumatra, Bangka, Java and Borneo**

STATUS
**Fairly common**

Binturong

# BIRD-EATING SPIDER

Among the largest of all spiders are the so-called bird-eating spiders of the family Theraphosidae. The largest species, from the Amazon basin, can attain a length of 3½ inches (9 cm) and a leg span of up to 10 inches (25 cm). Both the body and legs are very hairy. The theraphosids belong to the suborder Orthognatha, members of which can also correctly be referred to as the Mygalomorphae. Theraphosids differ from the more numerous and generally smaller Araneomorphae in having four lungs instead of two, four spinnerets instead of six and jaws that work vertically instead of sideways.

There are more than 600 species of bird-eating spider, all of which live in the Tropics. A number of other spiders, in related families, have also been called bird-eaters, and there are yet more species, only distantly related, that are referred to by this name. Some trapdoor spiders, for example, will kill small birds, and a number of spiders in the genus *Nephila* spin such a stout web that small birds are occasionally trapped and eaten. A further confusion is that bird-eating spiders are sometimes called tarantulas, especially by American writers. The true tarantula is in fact a species of wolf spider, *Lycosa tarentula*, found in southern Europe.

## Hairy hunters of the night
During the day bird-eating spiders shelter inside a rock crevice, a cavity in a tree or a silky burrow in the forest floor. They emerge at night to hunt but do not spin a web, instead running down prey or seizing it in a silent dash from their hiding place. In some species the legs spread as wide as the span of a human hand, and these spiders are strong enough to catch rodents and drag hummingbirds from their nests.

In spite of the size of bird-eating spiders, they are not especially dangerous to humans. The spiders are not easily provoked into attack, and their venom is usually no more troublesome than a bee sting. On the other hand, the entire body and legs are covered with fine hairs that have a powerful irritant effect on human skin. A curator of the invertebrate house at London Zoo was once injured so badly by handling a bird-eating spider that his hand was red, swollen and painful for several days and one of his fingers remained permanently crooked.

Most types of spider feed by injecting prey with powerful digestive juices, which liquefy the victim's body, and then sucking out the contents. Once a bird-eating spider has captured its prey, it stabs the victim with its sharply pointed hollow fangs and injects a fluid. It is not clear whether this fluid is a venom or merely the first of a series of injections of digestive juices. It is said to be very mild as a poison, neither killing nor paralyzing the prey. Bird-eating spiders sometimes appear to chew their food, but the movements mistaken for chewing are in fact repeated insertions of the fangs to liquefy more and more of the victim's body during the extended feeding process.

## Risky courtship
The instinct to attack moving animals is so strong in bird-eating spiders that the male has to approach the female very cautiously during the brief courtship. To avoid being eaten, he grasps her fangs with his front legs, and after mating he eases himself away from her, then hastily retreats. It is not known whether males find mates by smell or touch, but bird-eating spiders have poor eyesight.

The life cycle of bird-eating spiders varies between different species and environments. Each female lays 500 to 1,000 eggs in summer, in a loose cocoon, which she guards by resting with her front feet on it. If disturbed, the female

*One of the larger species of bird-eating spider,* Citharischius crawshayi, *at the entrance to its silk-lined burrow.*

*A covering of irritant hairs on the legs and body repels most would-be attackers of bird-eating spiders.*

## BIRD-EATING SPIDER

| | |
|---|---|
| PHYLUM | **Arthropoda** |
| CLASS | **Arachnida** |
| ORDER | **Araneae** |
| FAMILY | **Theraphosidae** |
| GENUS AND SPECIES | ***Theraphosa leblondi*** |

ALTERNATIVE NAMES
**Goliath tarantula; mygale**

LENGTH
**Abdomen: up to 4 in. (10 cm); leg span: up to 10 in. (25 cm)**

DISTINCTIVE FEATURES
**Very large size; large fangs; covering of fine, irritant hairs on body and legs**

DIET
**Adult: mainly large invertebrates; some birds and small mammals. Young: small insects.**

BREEDING
**Number of eggs: 500 to 1,000; hatching period: about 3 weeks; young leave cocoon within 5 weeks**

LIFE SPAN
**Up to 17 years, usually much less**

HABITAT
**Forest floor; construct silk-lined burrow**

DISTRIBUTION
**South America**

STATUS
**Not known**

spreads her fangs in a threatening posture. After about 3 weeks white baby spiders hatch from the eggs but stay in the cocoon for up to 5 weeks. The young are brown by the time they leave the cocoon, and stay nearby for a further 3–12 days before scattering.

Baby bird-eating spiders feed at first on very small, slow-moving insects, and they grow from ¹⁄₁₀ inch (4 mm) to ½ inch (15 mm) in the first 3 years. When adult, the spiders have been known to fast for nearly 2 years; and they may live for as long as 17 years. They molt four times in each of the first 3 years, twice in each of the fourth and fifth years, and after that once a year. During the molt the senses of sight, hearing and touch are suspended, and the spider remains motionless for several hours.

## Unusual defense mechanism

Bird-eating spiders have relatively few predators, largely, it is claimed, because of the irritant nature of their hairs. It has been suggested that a spider scrapes its abdomen with its hind legs to release a cloud of fine hairs that blinds and stifles its pursuer. The spiders are most likely to fall victim to parasites, fungal infections and large predators. And, in spite of the parental care enjoyed during the first weeks of life, it has been estimated that not more than 0.2 percent of the young reach adulthood.

## An artist vindicated

The first person to record the predatory habits of bird-eating spiders was Maria Sibilla Merian. In 1705 she published in Amsterdam, in the Netherlands, a large book called "*Metamorphosis Insectorum Surinamensium*." Merian was an artist working in what was then Dutch Guiana—modern Suriname—in northeastern South America. Her book, which was mainly devoted to invertebrates, included a picture showing a large bird-eating spider dragging a hummingbird from its nest. Beside the picture was an account of how the spiders routinely catch small birds and suck their juices.

No one believed that this was possible until the second half of the 19th century, and in the meantime several well-known zoologists made vitriolic attacks on the book. At last, in 1863, a scientist was able to watch bird-eating spiders killing small finches in the Amazon basin in South America and Merian's account was finally accepted as fact.

# BIRD OF PARADISE

THE BIRDS OF PARADISE are 45 species in the family Paradisaeidae and include some of the most colorful and ornate of all birds. The family has a very restricted distribution, being confined to the humid rain forests of New Guinea and neighboring small islands, such as the Moluccas, with the exception of four species found in mountain forests in northeastern Australia.

Birds of paradise are descended from less colorful, crowlike ancestors. They still resemble crows in having stout bills, strong feet and compact bodies, but the males have evolved a remarkable array of plumages. Many male birds of paradise have elongated, lacy or wirelike plumes extending well beyond the tail at rest, but these are trailed over the back in a superb, fanlike spread during their courtship displays. The fabulous breeding rituals have yet to be observed in some species.

Many birds of paradise have names that hark back to Europe's colonial past. Examples include the King of Saxony bird of paradise (*Pteridophora alberti*), the Emperor bird of paradise (*Paradisaea guilielmi*), Prince Rudolf's blue bird of paradise (*Paradisaea rudolphi*), Princess Stephanie's astrapia (*Astrapia stephaniae*) and the Prince Albert, or magnificent, riflebird (*Ptiloris magnificus*).

## Exotic discoveries

Birds of paradise have been known to the Western world since 1522, when the sole surviving ship of Ferdinand Magellan's small fleet returned to Spain. Among the treasures it brought back were some bird of paradise skins as a present from a sultan in the Moluccas to the King of Spain. The feathers were so bright and fine that the Spaniards believed the birds must have come from paradise and named them accordingly.

The birds remained almost unknown in the wild to Westerners, but because of their brilliant plumage they became popular as material for the millinery trade. The skins came from unknown sources in the East Indies, and in the latter part of the 19th century an estimated 50,000 skins were arriving in Western markets every year. Birds of paradise soon acquired a virtually mythical status in Europe and North America.

The King of Saxony bird of paradise was discovered in a Paris market in 1894. It had such strange plumage that some ornithologists refused to believe it was real, since making of "artifacts" by grafting feathers from one species on to the plumage of others was a common practice in the bird of paradise business. This small bird, only 7 inches (18 cm) long, has two 18-inch (46 cm) plumes trailing from the back of its head. Each plume is made up of 30 or 40 separate "flags," rather like bunting, which are brilliant blue on the outside and brown on the inside.

*A displaying male lesser bird of paradise, Paradisaea minor, spreads its wings and raises its tail feathers. It is one of the most resplendent members of a spectacular family.*

*A female crested bird of paradise,* Cnemophilus macgregorii, *feeds her single chick. Female birds of paradise tend to be unobtrusive and plainer than the males.*

## BIRDS OF PARADISE

| | |
|---|---|
| CLASS | **Aves** |
| ORDER | **Passeriformes** |
| FAMILY | **Paradisaeidae** |
| GENUS | **18, including *Paradisaea, Ptiloris, Pteridophora, Cicinnarus* and *Cnemophilus*** |
| SPECIES | **45, including Raggiana bird of paradise, *Paradisaea raggiana*; Emperor bird of paradise, *P. guilielmi*; and magnificent bird of paradise, *Cicinnarus magnificus*** |

LENGTH
**Head to tail: 6–44 in. (15–110 cm)**

DISTINCTIVE FEATURES
**Males of many species have elaborate and colorful plumage; females much plainer**

DIET
**Mainly fruits; also insects, leaves, buds, nectar, tree frogs, lizards and bird nestlings**

BREEDING
**Age at first breeding: 4–7 years (male), probably 2–4 years (female); number of eggs: usually 1 or 2; incubation period: 17–21 days; fledging period: 17–30 days**

HABITAT
**Tropical rain forest**

DISTRIBUTION
**New Guinea, Moluccan Islands and northeastern Australia**

STATUS
**Vulnerable: 6 species; near-threatened: 8 species; several other species declining**

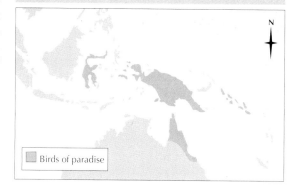

Birds of paradise

## Difference between the sexes

A few birds of paradise have relatively common-place plumage. In such species males and females are very much alike, their appearance enlivened only by wattles or a gloss to some of the feathers. The more typical birds of paradise exhibit a marked sexual dimorphism, that is, the plumage of male and female differ. The females are not colorful, while the males are resplendent in fine feathers. It is usually the tail that is developed into elaborate and beautiful plumes and sprays. A good example is the greater bird of paradise, *Paradisaea apoda*, which is distinguished by a mass of red plumes trailing from the flanks and two thin "wires" dangling from the tail.

In typical birds of paradise the male plays the minimum part necessary for the raising of a family. His only role is to attract and fertilize a female. After mating she leaves him to build the nest and rears her young alone.

## Dramatic displays

Some birds of paradise display singly in small arenas that they clear of vegetation. Other species display communally at traditional sites known as leks. As many as 40 birds of paradise have been seen displaying in one tree. To attract females, the plumes are erected and displayed like those of the peacock and lyrebird. Birds of paradise also use song to attract females and this may be heard up to ⅔ miles (1 km) away.

Courtship has been extensively studied in the raggiana bird of paradise, *Paradisaea raggiana*. The males have orange or reddish plumes on their flanks, a green throat and a yellow cowl. Up to 10 gather in a lek to attract females, sometimes returning each breeding season to the same lek. The composition of these display groups may remain largely the same for over 10 years.

The male raggiana birds of paradise sing to attract females and only begin their performance when one or more females has approached. They move rapidly from perch to perch, spreading their wings. The upper surface of the wings are beaten together and the chest is lowered and raised. Females move about the lek while the now-stationary males continue to lower their heads and beat their wings. After mating, the females build a flimsy looking nest of plant fibers, rootlets, leaves and vine tendrils and lay one or two eggs. Incubation takes 18–20 days in this species, the young hatching pink and naked. They are looked after by the female alone.

Male riflebirds in the genus *Ptiloris*, from northern Australia and New Guinea, are so called because their two-note call is said to be like the whistle of a passing bullet. They display in trees. A male perches, calling at intervals until a female appears. He then spreads its glossy black wings, curving them around until the tips meet in front of its head, and throws back its head to reveal shiny blue neck feathers. At the same time he rocks from side to side and the female faces him, spreads her wings and copies his actions. Eventually there is a wild chase through the trees, followed by mating.

In several birds of paradise the males hang upside down from their display perches to ensure that watching females get the best possible view of their plumage. Both the Emperor bird of paradise and the rare Prince Rudolf's blue bird of paradise adopt this strategy.

Research into birds of paradise has concentrated on display systems and sexual selection, and their nesting and feeding behavior is still poorly known. Nests have only been found for a few species. These are usually bulky bowls of twigs on branches or rocks. Birds of paradise feed mainly on fruits, supplemented with leaves, buds, nectar and some animal prey.

## Fashion victims

The prime enemies of birds of paradise in the past have been humans. The indigenous people of New Guinea have long used bird-of-paradise plumes in ornamental headdresses. Bird-of-paradise plumes have also been exported, first to Asian merchants, later directly to Europe and America, where the demand became so great that stocks were severely jeopardized. The extent of the damage is not known, but many once-common species are now rare and others could well be extinct. Eventually public opinion swung against the feather trade. It became illegal to import skins into the United States and many European countries and in the 1920s, export from New Guinea was prohibited, with the result that many species are now recovering.

*A male Emperor bird of paradise calls to attract a mate. Should a female arrive, he will court her by hanging upside down from a branch to show off his finery.*

# BIRDS OF PREY

*The genus Falco, or falcons, includes some of the fastest and most aerobatic birds of prey, such as the Aplomado falcon, Falco femoralis.*

IRDS OF PREY HAVE hooked bills, powerful legs and feet, generally with sharp, curved claws, and keen vision. These features are adaptations to a lifestyle dependent to varying degrees on hunting living prey, scavenging carrion and tearing flesh. Birds of prey belong to the order Falconiformes, which comprises two large families, the Accipitridae (hawks and eagles) and the Falconidae (falcons and caracaras), and two families each containing a single species, the Pandionidae (osprey) and the Sagittariidae (secretary bird). The Falconiformes also include the vultures, discussed elsewhere, which many authorities consider to have closer affinities with the storks. Another group sometimes described as birds of prey are the mainly nocturnal owls.

## A long history

Fossil fragments of a tiny, falcon-type bird have been reported from lower Eocene deposits in England, apparently dating back 55 million years. Better-documented palaeontological evidence relates to buzzard-type fossils found in French and Argentinian rocks of 30 million to 50 million years of age, and to distant ancestors of today's falcons found in France that are thought to date back 36 million years.

Today the birds of prey, or raptors, are a cosmopolitan group, represented in every continent except Antarctica, and in almost every ecological niche imaginable. While the greatest species concentrations are to be found in tropical forests, there are raptors that hunt primarily over the sea, others found at great altitudes in mountain ranges and still more adapted to hunting in desert environments. Some of the more versatile species with varied, nonspecialist diets and feeding techniques can thrive in towns and cities and thus benefit from urbanization.

## Size matters

The range of size exhibited by birds of prey is extraordinary. The black-thighed falconet, *Microhierax fringillarius*, of Indonesia, for example, can weigh as little as 1¼ ounces (35 g) and have a wingspan of less than 1 foot (30 cm), while the harpy eagle, *Harpia harpyja*, of Central and South America weighs up to 20 pounds (9 kg) and the bald eagle, *Haliaeetus leucocephalus*, may reach 14 pounds (6 kg). Several species of eagle, which need massive wings to allow them to soar for long periods, have wingspans of 7 feet (2.3 m).

In most species of bird the male is larger than the female, but this trend is reversed in many birds of prey. It is generally the case that the more aggressive the species of raptor, and particularly the greater the proportion of birds in its diet, the greater the size difference between the sexes. A female goshawk, *Accipiter gentilis*, may weigh twice as much as her male partner. One theory is that size difference in birds of prey reduces the competition for food between the sexes, since the larger females are able to hunt more substantial prey.

It has been suggested that female raptors are larger than males to increase breeding success. Females may need to be larger to accumulate sufficient energy to produce eggs, and large size may enable them to survive for longer periods without food while incubating. A big female is also in a better position to

---

### CLASSIFICATION

**CLASS**
Aves

**ORDER**
Falconiformes

**NUMBER OF SPECIES**
Family Pandionidae: 1
Family Accipitridae: 223
Family Sagittariidae: 1
Family Falconidae: 61

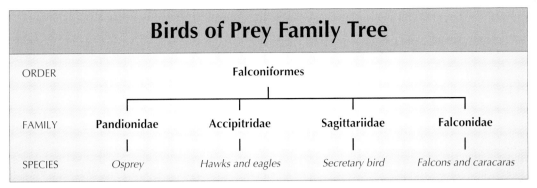

## Birds of Prey Family Tree

| ORDER | | | Falconiformes | | | |
|---|---|---|---|---|---|---|
| FAMILY | Pandionidae | | Accipitridae | | Sagittariidae | Falconidae |
| SPECIES | *Osprey* | | *Hawks and eagles* | | *Secretary bird* | *Falcons and caracaras* |

### Soaring high

Many of the other raptors are "searchers," rather than "chasers." These species use their mastery of the air to soar or hover, scanning the ground below for animals to pounce on, or for carcasses to scavenge. Raptors that have adopted a "searching" hunting strategy tend to have broad wings for their size. This design is suited to staying airborne for long periods while using relatively small amounts of energy, instead of providing short bursts of energetic, rapid-pursuit flight. Eagles, buzzards and many kites are typical soaring birds, while the American kestrel (*Falco sparverius*), white-tailed kite (*Elanus leucurus*) and rough-legged buzzard (*Buteo lagopus*) are three examples of raptors that regularly hover.

### Specialist hunters

Some birds of prey have developed very specialized feeding requirements. For example, the honey buzzard, *Pernis apivorus*, feeds largely on wasps' and bees' nests; the Everglade snail kite, *Rostrhamus sociabilis*, preys on aquatic snails; and the harpy eagle snatches fully grown monkeys and sloths from the canopy of rain forest trees.

Specialist diets demand a range of special adaptations. The osprey, the sole representative of the Pandionidae family, is a superb fisher, plunging into fresh or salt water to grasp prey. To help it grip struggling fish, it has very long talons and

protect herself and her young. The main threat is attack by aggressive males of the same species, particularly males in neighboring territories and nonbreeding males without a mate of their own.

Mate selection is another factor that may tend to increase female size in relation to males. Smaller, lightweight males are likely to be more agile, which would make them better hunters and therefore better at providing food for females and their young; it follows that female raptors may prefer to mate with smaller partners. Over time, large males would have been selected against because they are less successful at finding a mate and fathering young.

### Aerial pursuits

The feeding methods employed by birds of prey are as diverse as the habitats they occupy. Many species, particularly those in the family Falconidae, take their prey on the wing, and for this they need to be active and agile fliers. These raptors have long, strongly tapering wings and a highly muscular structure, with the chest, or pectoral, muscles often accounting for a large part of their body weight. For example, about 20 percent of the body weight of the peregrine falcon, *Falco peregrinus*, is made up of these muscles. This species employs a hunting strategy demanding strength and athleticism: it swoops at flying birds at speeds of 120 miles per hour (180 km/h).

Raptors that chase and catch prey while on the wing often consume the food in midair. Prey is snatched with the talons (claws) and passed up to the bill. Common prey items are small to medium-sized birds and large flying insects, especially dragonflies and beetles. More unusual aerial prey includes bats, which are caught at dusk when they emerge from their daytime roosts.

*Birds of prey exhibit a tremendous range of form. The African pygmy falcon,* **Polihierax semitorquatus,** *is a tiny species measuring just 6½ inches (16.5 cm) and preys mainly on insects.*

*The long legs of the savanna hawk,* Heterospizias meridionalis, *indicate that it is a snake-hunter. Like several other raptors, it takes advantage of bush fires to catch animals fleeing the flames.*

the equator and may migrate 19,000 miles (30,000 km) during the course of a year.

Most soaring raptors are incapable of long-distance, active flight and are therefore dependent on being kept aloft by upward currents of warm air, known as thermals. These currents develop only over land, and migrating eagles, buzzards and hawks try to avoid or minimize journeys over the sea. This leads to big concentrations of birds of prey in spring and especially the fall as the birds are funneled toward narrow sea crossings, or isthmuses.

Notable places to watch for these mass movements include Panama, Eilat in southernmost Israel, Istanbul in Turkey and Veracruz in Mexico, where more than half a million birds of prey have been logged in a single day in the fall. Some inland locations on the regular routes taken by migrating raptors also offer excellent views of the spectacle, and in the United States such watchpoints include Point Pelee, on the northern shore of Lake Erie in Ontario, Cape May in New Jersey and "Hawk Mountain" in Pennsylvania.

feet covered with tiny spines, and it also has a dense plumage to provide protection when diving into the water. The secretary bird, *Sagittarius serpentarius*, of the other single-species raptor family, the Sagittariidae, has very long legs for kicking snakes to death. An exclusively terrestrial hunter, the secretary bird has forgone flight altogether as a means of locating and catching prey. The bat hawk, *Machaerhamphus alcinus*, of Africa and Southeast Asia, hunts bats at nightfall and has large eyes adapted to the low-light conditions.

## Territory defenders

Nearly all birds of prey are territorial. Even the group-nesting Eleonora's falcon, *Falco eleonorae*, has a territory of a few square yards, which it defends against others in the colony. However, large territories are more typical. The larger raptors and those that live in habitats where the availability of prey is low tend to have the largest territories of all. A gyrfalcon, *F. rusticolus*, territory in the tundra wastes of northern Canada can cover 380 square miles (1,000 sq km).

Aerial display flights are performed by the males of many species, and the females also participate in some. The highly visible displays serve a variety of purposes, including the attraction of a mate, the strengthening of the pair-bond and the demonstration of territory-ownership.

## On the move

Birds of prey from high, northern latitudes tend to move south in the fall as food becomes scarce. Gyrfalcons, which breed further north than any other species of raptors, have been tracked moving over 2,100 miles (3,400 km) during the fall, and many individuals of this species fly even greater distances. Some Northern Hemisphere species winter south of

## Conservation

Certain species of raptors, particularly the scavengers and those that benefit from forest clearance, have been helped by human activities. However, many others are threatened by habitat destruction, by hunting and other forms of human persecution, and by pesticides that diminish breeding success. Conservationists have nevertheless had successes, notably with the peregrine falcon. Its population has recovered as a result of tighter controls on the use of pesticides.

The greatest raptor conservation success story concerns the Mauritius kestrel, *Falco punctatus*, of the Indian Ocean island of Mauritius. Its population had fallen to four birds by the early 1970s due to habitat loss, pesticide use and predation by introduced rats and cats. Conservationists trapped the alien predators, erected nest boxes to improve breeding success, left out food supplements and released kestrels in alternative habitats. There are now several hundred Mauritius kestrels.

*For particular species see:*
- BALD EAGLE • BUZZARD • CROWNED EAGLE
- EVERGLADE SNAIL KITE • FISH EAGLE
- GOLDEN EAGLE • GOSHAWK • GYRFALCON
- HARPY EAGLE • HARRIER • HOBBY
- HONEY BUZZARD • KESTREL • KITE • MARTIAL EAGLE
- MERLIN • OSPREY • PEREGRINE FALCON
- SECRETARY BIRD • SPARROW HAWK

# BIRDWING

THE WINGSPAN OF birdwing butterflies often exceeds the length of a fully outstretched human hand. The Queen Alexandra's birdwing, which has a wingspan of 6¾–11 inches (17–28 cm), is the largest known butterfly in the world. It was the remarkable wingspan of some of the birdwing genera that provoked naturalists to dub them *Ornithoptera*, meaning "bird-winged."

## Sexual selection

The width and size of birdwings is due to their long, graceful forewings. The hind wings, by comparison, are small. The adaptive significance of such large forewings is much debated, but seems likely to be connected with sexual selection. Outsized forewings may impress female birdwing butterflies in much the same way as the tails of male peacocks impress the females of that species. According to this theory the forewings provide female butterflies with a visible indication of male fitness, and therefore also of the quality of the male genes. Other theories are that large forewings assist in thermoregulation (the way in which an animal regulates its body temperature), or that they improve aerodynamics.

One characteristic shown by many members of the swallowtail family, Papilionidae, to which birdwings belong, is a long tail on each of the hind wings. These tails are not present in every species of birdwing, but can be seen in the tailed birdwing, *Troides paradisea*.

## Vibrant patterns

Birdwings appear to have velvety wings, and shades of black and purple feature prominently. Many species have iridescent markings in blue, green, pink, orange or gold. Females tend to have less spectacular markings, and their wings are often speckled with a uniform white instead of the fluctuating color ranges of males. However, some females have bright colors. For example, the female Cairns birdwing has black wings with white markings, while the female Rajah Brooke's birdwing, *T. brookiana*, varies from olive-green with white or green markings to black with coppery-green markings.

Butterfly collectors named several birdwings after their heroes. One was named after Queen Victoria: Queen Victoria's birdwing, *T. victoriae*, is found on the New Georgia archipelago of the

Solomon Islands. Rajah Brooke of Sarawak had the honor of having perhaps the most striking of all birdwings named after him.

## Entomologists fooled

Birdwings live in rain forest, from China, India and Sri Lanka south to northern Australia, New Guinea and the Solomon Islands. Very little is known about some of the species.

For a long time, entomologists listed, as one of the distinctive features of Rajah Brooke's birdwing, the fact that the female was rarely seen. They even put the ratio of males to females at 1,000:1. The entomologists based their statistics on data obtained from collections made at sites where birdwings congregate, such as riverbanks, seepages and other damp places. Then it became apparent that the reason for these remarkable figures was that only the males of the species gathered at these spots. In other birdwing species, the ratio between the sexes was evenly balanced. In fact, females of the common birdwing, *T. helena*, are more numerous than the males.

Birdwings live in trees, especially in the canopy of foliage at the tops of the taller trees. However, when birdwings do fly low they are easy to catch because their flight relatively slow and direct. This is in contrast to the bouncing, weaving flight of many other butterflies.

*Rajah Brooke's birdwing is the national butterfly of Malaysia. Its caterpillars have yet to be discovered in the wild.*

*Large wings and colorful markings make birdwings among the most distinctive of all butterflies.*

## BIRDWINGS

CLASS    **Insecta**

ORDER    **Lepidoptera**

FAMILY   **Papilionidae**

GENUS    ***Troides, Trogonoptera* and *Ornithoptera***

SPECIES   **About 30, including common birdwing, *Troides helena*; Rajah Brooke's birdwing, *T. brookiana*; and Queen Victoria's birdwing *T. victoriae***

LENGTH
**Wingspan: 6¾–11 in. (17–28 cm) in largest species**

DISTINCTIVE FEATURES
**Very large wingspan; forewings much larger than hind wings; bold, metallic or iridescent markings, strongest in male**

DIET
**Adult: flower nectar. Larva: leaves of rain forest vines and betel plant.**

BREEDING
**Poorly known**

HABITAT
**Tropical rain forest**

DISTRIBUTION
**Mainland Asia south through Indonesia and New Guinea to Solomon Islands and northern Australia**

STATUS
**Many species endangered or threatened**

Birdwings

## Deterring predators

Adult birdwings feed on the nectar of flowers. The caterpillars feed on forest vines in the *Aristolochiaceae* family and on betel leaves. However, the ongoing destruction of rain forest containing these vines, for urban development, forestry projects and farming, is threatening the survival of some birdwing species. Some of the closely related swallowtail butterflies also feed on plants of the same family. Swallowtails are known to be distasteful to predators because of a chemical contained in their food plants, and some birdwing caterpillars are distasteful to their own predators for the same reason.

A further defensive adaptation is the Y-shaped organ, called an osmeterium, located on the caterpillar's head. It is joined to glands in the body and exudes chemicals which have a smell that repels predators. The common birdwing has distinctive black and yellow markings warning potential predators of its unpleasant taste.

The life cycle of birdwing butterflies varies according to the species. The eggs of the common birdwing are laid singly on the upper sides of leaves. From the eggs hatch caterpillars bearing six rows of fleshy tubercles (prominent bumps or nodules), which run the whole length of the body. After the caterpillars have fed for a month, they turn into pupae on the vertical stem of the plant where they have been living. The pupa's lower end is anchored to the plant stem by a silken pad. The body and upper end of the pupa are supported by a silk thread, which passes around the stem of the plant.

## Prized by collectors

In 1966 a large butterfly collection was auctioned in Paris and $1,800 was paid for a specimen of a rare birdwing species, *T. allotai*, from the Solomon Islands. The high prices paid by collectors create a lucrative trade in butterflies. Some birdwings are bred to sell, but others are collected in the wild. Many species are now threatened, especially those with a limited distribution. All of the birdwings are now protected by law: none can be collected without a permit and some cannot be collected at all.

# BISHOP BIRD

THE BISHOPS are one of several groups of birds collectively called weavers. Other weavers include the malimbes, buffalo-weavers, queleas and widow birds. Nine species have bishop in their name, and they share the genus *Euplectes* with eight species of widow bird.

Bishops generally have a rather dull nonbreeding plumage. The females look similar during the breeding season, while the males molt into a brightly colored plumage that makes them popular as cage birds. Red, orange, yellow and black feature prominently in breeding males of the various species. The fire-crowned bishop, *E. hordeaceus*, is a little smaller than a sparrow, and in breeding plumage the male's crown, nape, breast and back are orange-red, contrasting with glossy black on the belly, flight feathers and tail.

## Grassland specialists
Bishops are found in the tropical and subtropical regions of Africa, often in open savanna and forest clearings, and especially in damp areas of thick vegetation. A few species are found in other habitats. For instance, Burton's black-and-yellow bishop, *E. capensis*, which is also known as the yellow-shouldered widow bird, lives in high mountain grasslands at 4,000–9,500 feet (1,220–2,900 m). It was discovered by Sir Richard Francis Burton, an explorer better known as the translator of the "*Arabian Nights*." The golden-backed bishop, *E. aurea*, was once thought to be confined to the island of Sao Tomé, in the Gulf of Guinea, but another population has now been found on the nearby coast of Angola, in central Africa.

Outside the breeding season, bishops associate in flocks. It can be difficult to tell the sexes apart at this time. In the evening the flocks move to a favorite drinking place, often where bushes overhang a pond or stream, before retiring to a communal roost. Bishops feed on seeds and insects, especially termites. Flocks may descend on crops and prove to be a pest, but bishops are not such a threat to agriculture as other members of the weaver family.

## Colorful courtship displays
At the beginning of the breeding season, in May or June, male bishops leave the flocks and set up territories. These are defended against other males by agitated and frequently aggressive patrols, and females are attracted by the males' displays. The male perches on the top of a grass stem or bush and puffs out his brilliant plumage, showing it off to best effect. In contrast to this visual display, the song is weak, consisting of a few metallic notes. Often the bishop sings while flying from one perch to another with characteristically slow wing beats that are quite different from the normal, rapid flight. The small yellow-crowned bishop, *E. afer*, raises the yellow feathers on its back and flies about its territory looking like a large bumblebee.

Having established a territory, the male begins to make a nest from grasses a few feet above the ground. First he makes a horizontal ring, then builds a vertical arch over it. This is the framework to which more grass is added to make a globular nest, with the entrance in one side. The yellow-crowned bishop nests low in the aquatic plants of swamps around lakes and rivers; the nests are often swept away in floods.

The female is courted during nest-building. She alone sits on the clutch of two to four eggs, and once incubation has begun the male starts another nest and courts another female. Females seem unaware of territorial limits, whereas males rarely venture beyond the boundaries of their territories. A male spends much time keeping other males and females out of his territory and greeting his mates with a twittering call.

*Male bishops, such as this red bishop, Euplectes orix, weave a complex ball-shaped nest complete with domed roof.*

*During their courtship display male red bishops perch atop grass stems so that their fiery plumage stands out like a beacon against their surroundings.*

## FIRE-CROWNED BISHOP

| | |
|---|---|
| CLASS | **Aves** |
| ORDER | **Passeriformes** |
| FAMILY | **Ploceidae** |
| GENUS AND SPECIES | ***Euplectes hordeaceus*** |

ALTERNATIVE NAMES
**Black-winged bishop; black-winged red bishop; red-crowned bishop**

LENGTH
**Head to tail: 4¾ in. (12 cm)**

DISTINCTIVE FEATURES
**Male: reddish neck, back, rump and breast; black belly and tail. Female, nonbreeding male and juvenile: tawny breast band; yellowish stripe over eye.**

DIET
**Seeds and insects**

BREEDING
**Age at first breeding: 1 year; breeding season: May–July; number of eggs: 2 to 4; incubation period: about 14 days; fledging period: about 14 days; breeding interval: male mates with females in serial fashion**

LIFE SPAN
**Not known**

HABITAT
**Fields and damp grassland with bushes**

DISTRIBUTION
**Kenya and Tanzania**

STATUS
**Common**

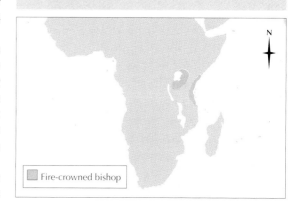
Fire-crowned bishop

During this time the female bishops are busy rearing their broods. In the incubation period they strengthen the nest, making a porch over the entrance and adding material to the floor, which is so thin at first that the eggs can be seen through it. The hot sun and enclosed nest keep the eggs warm during the day, so they need incubating only at night. Incubation and fledging take a little over 2 weeks each.

## Bigamous bishops

Most birds are apparently monogamous, taking only one mate, and both members of a pair usually help to care for the offspring. However, relatively few birds mate for life; examples include the swans and albatrosses. The majority breed with a different partner each year. Moreover, most of the so-called monogamous species also indulge in extra-pair copulations, in which birds "cheat" on their regular mate for that year. The result is that some clutches of eggs are of mixed paternity.

Bishops are among the few polygamous birds. This term refers to a state in which a single bird of either sex has a relationship with two or more birds of the opposite sex. In the case of the bishops, one male mates with up to six females; this practice is known as polygyny. Other polygamous species indulge in polyandry, in which one female mates with two or more males.

Polygyny seems to have several advantages for bishops. Females outnumber males in certain species of bishop, so monogamous breeding would mean that some females would not be able to find a mate. Polygyny enables the surplus females to raise broods, and is possible because in bishops the females do not need any help in feeding their chicks. The building of enclosed nests may be an adaptation to polygamous breeding. Female bishops have to leave the nest to forage for their nestlings and, without a male taking turns in brooding, young in an open nest would soon get cold and be exposed to predators. Covered nests provide both insulation and protection for the fatherless nestlings.

# BISON

Bison are large and oxlike, the adults weighing up to 2,200 pounds (1,000 kg). The largest bison stand 6 feet (1.8 m) at the shoulder, which is raised in a distinct hump, giving a very hunchbacked appearance. The hair on head, neck, shoulders and forelegs is long and shaggy. The broad forehead is flanked by two short, curving horns in both sexes.

The two species of bison extant today are the European bison, *Bison bonasus*, or wisent, and the American bison, *B. bison*, often incorrectly called the buffalo. The latter name strictly belongs to the Cape buffalo of Africa. The European bison has a shorter coat, larger, more curved horns and larger hindquarters than its American relative. There are two subspecies of American bison. The plains bison, *B. b. bison*, of the United States, is smaller and lighter in color than the wood bison, *B. b. athabascae*, of Canada, but its head and shoulders are more stocky. Of the two, the wood bison resembles the European bison more closely.

## Divergence of the bison

Bison probably once roamed across Europe, Asia and North America. This theory is supported by the similarity between the wood bison and the European bison, both of which live in woodlands. The European bison is now thought to have crossed into Asia and Europe from North America at the end of the Ice Age, traveling across what is now the Bering Strait but was once a land bridge. This view is contrary to the common assumption that the American species is a descendant of the European species.

## Senseless slaughter

Some 50 million bison once roamed North America but by 1889 a mere 540 were left. The massacre of the North American bison is matched by the extinction of the passenger pigeon, *Ectopistes migratorius*, also of North America. Both once appeared to exist in limitless numbers but both succumbed to organized slaughter backed by modern techniques.

When Europeans first settled in North America, bison ranged from northern Canada as far south as the border of Mexico and across the continent east from the Rocky Mountains. The bison were apparently increasing in numbers and it is thought that they would have spread through the passes of the Rockies and onto the plains of the Pacific coast. However, with the coming of Europeans, they were hunted so relentlessly that they nearly became extinct.

Bison had always played a vital part in the economy of Native Americans, but relatively few bison were killed. Native Americans became more efficient bison hunters after the introduction of horses by the Spanish conquistadors. Later, European settlers spread across the plains, killing

*Today most North American bison are confined to national parks. This bull is one of the 1,500 to 2,000 bison that live in Yellowstone National Park, Wyoming.*

*Bison calves stay with their mother for 2–3 years. They are born in late spring and soon develop the thick coat that will protect them in the coming winter.*

bison for meat and hides, and large-scale hunts were organized to get meat for railroad construction workers. The railroads opened up a new market in the East for bison hides and tongues, while bison bones were ground to make fertilizer for the corn-growing prairies.

Bison were also killed for sport. Daily bags of 50 or 60 seem to have been common, and totals of more than 100 bison shot by a single hunter in one day were claimed. The carcasses were usually left to rot, without any meat or a single hide being collected. The effect of this slaughter is not mitigated by the fact that the spread of agriculture would eventually have decimated the herds by taking away their grazing lands.

The European bison also suffered a catastrophic fall in numbers, but its decline occurred over a period of centuries. The principal cause of its demise was the felling of forests in which it roamed. The last truly wild European bison lived in the Bialowieza Forest, Poland, but were devastated in World War I and during the upheavals that followed. Only about 30 bison survived, all of which were in zoos. Careful management enabled numbers of European bison to rise again, reaching 360 in 1959, including a herd in a reserve established in Bialowieza. The population stood at 790 to 800 in 1965, and there are now 2,700 European bison.

Today the future of the North American bison is also more secure. Indeed, the population of the plains bison is sufficiently healthy to allow hunting under license. In Canada the last wood bison are fully protected in a reserve in Alberta, the Wood Buffalo National Park.

## Smaller herds

Bison live in herds, in the past numbering thousands of individuals but now much smaller. The basic social grouping comprises a bull together with a cow and her offspring. The cow is the leader of family groups such as this.

# BISON

| | |
|---|---|
| CLASS | **Mammalia** |
| ORDER | **Artiodactyla** |
| FAMILY | **Bovidae** |

GENUS AND SPECIES   **American bison, *Bison bison*; European bison, *B. bonasus***

ALTERNATIVE NAMES
***B. bison bison*: plains bison; *B. b. athabascae*: wood bison; *B. bonasus*: wisent**

WEIGHT
**770–2,200 lb. (350–1,000 kg)**

LENGTH
**Head and body: 83–138 in. (2.1–3.5 m); shoulder height: 59–79 in. (1.5–2 m)**

DISTINCTIVE FEATURES
**Hunched back; shaggy hair on neck, shoulders and forelegs; short, curved horns**

DIET
**Grasses, herbs, bark, shoots and acorns**

BREEDING
**Age at first breeding: 2–4 years; breeding season: July–September; number of young: 1; gestation period: 285 days (American bison), 260–270 days (European bison); breeding interval: 1–2 years**

LIFE SPAN
**Up to 40 years**

HABITAT
**American bison: prairie, mountains and forest. European bison: woods and grassland.**

DISTRIBUTION
**American bison: mainly western and central North America. European bison: Poland, Lithuania, Belarus and European Russia.**

STATUS
**American bison: population at least 100,000. European bison: endangered; population: 2,700.**

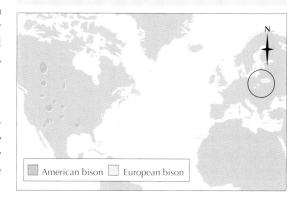

American bison   European bison

North American bison feed mainly on grasses and herbs, making long seasonal migrations to find the best grazing areas, which vary with the seasons. They supplement this diet with the bark and shoots of different trees. Bark is more important to European bison, in particular that of sallow, poplar and aspen trees. The shoots of young evergreens are also sometimes browsed, and in the fall acorns are a favorite food. Both species of bison are fond of wallowing in mud and rubbing themselves against trees and boulders.

## Battles for dominance

Mating takes place from July to September, when the males in a herd fight one another. The more successful males tend a female for several days during estrus, the period in which she is receptive, and prevent other males from approaching closer than 26 feet (8 m). Successful males are therefore able to almost monopolize sexual activity through consorting with females.

Bison have a gestation period of about 9 months, the calves being born from April to June. The cow leaves the herd to drop her calf and returns when it is able to walk. The entire herd assists in the defense of calves against their only natural enemy, the gray wolf. The calves are nursed for a year and stay with their mothers until they are sexually mature at 2–3 years.

## Relationship with humans

Bison were essential to many Native American tribes. The animals provided meat, both fresh and dried for later use; hides, for clothing, bedding, tents and canoes; dung, for fuel; and bones and sinews, for weapons, tools and utensils. The bison appeared in Native American religions as a powerful figure to be worshiped.

Native Americans had various rituals that were thought to ensure a plentiful supply of bison, for if the bison did not arrive on their annual migration the people would face a lean time. Native Americans believed that "buffalo" sprang up every year, and that it was necessary to lure them to hunting grounds. Bison skulls were considered to be extremely useful for this purpose, and were piled up or displayed in a prominent place because it was thought that the bison would seek out their "white-faced" companions. In other rites, oracles were consulted to find out where the bison were. The medicine men performing these services acquired great merit. They continued their ceremonies and incantations until the bison arrived, an inevitable event if the Native Americans were waiting on a regular migration route.

There came a time when the bison did fail to arrive. By the late 19th century Europeans had contrived virtually to wipe out North America's vast bison herds and the Native Americans starved as a result. To Native Americans, wanton killing of bison was a serious crime punishable by death. The loss of their livelihood combined with the loss of their territory caused them to resort to an armed struggle. Some enlightened Europeans sought to safeguard both the Native Americans and the herds of bison on which they depended, but others claimed that the extermination of bison was the only way of "civilizing" Native Americans.

*Huge herds of North American bison are a thing of the past, and compact family units are now the norm.*

# BITTERLING

*Bitterling have a remarkable way of breeding. In order to reproduce successfully each pair must find a freshwater mussel as a nursery for their eggs.*

THE BITTERLING is a minnowlike fish that grows to about 3½ inches (9 cm) long. Its name, taken from the German by aquarists, refers to the bitter taste of the flesh of this fish. The bitterling lives mainly in clear streams with clean sandy beds in central and eastern Europe and Asia Minor, and has been introduced to western Europe and New York State.

## Color signals

Normally the sexes look alike but during the spawning season the male bitterling becomes brilliantly colored. The normal coloration is greenish brown on the back with flanks and belly a gleaming silver. The dorsal fin is dark, the other fins are pale. When breeding the male turns olive on the back, his flanks becoming iridescent with all the colors of the rainbow, but with violet and blue predominant. The male's throat and belly are red or orange, his paired fins yellow, his tail fin green and yellow and his unpaired fins red with black edges. The female bitterling is more yellow and less iridescent.

The main food of the bitterling consists of small worms and midge larvae, although a variety of animal and plant food is taken. The worms, popularly known as pot worms because they are common among the roots of water plants cultivated in pots, are white, less than 1 inch (2.5 cm) long and related to earthworms.

## Mussel maternity wards

The story of the bitterling's breeding behavior is one of the most fascinating and well-studied examples of symbiosis, or mutualism, between two animal species. Bitterlings spawn in April, and for this the presence of a freshwater mussel is needed.

When the male bitterling adopts his bright colors, he also becomes excited and the female develops a pink tube that protrudes from her vent for ½ inches (13 mm). The male keeps close beside the female, and seems to be guiding her toward a freshwater mussel. He also drives away any other males coming near her. As the pair of fish swim around together, the female's tube, which is her egg-guide, or ovipositor, begins to lengthen, and in a few hours it grows to 2 inches (5 cm). The pair approach the chosen mussel and the female positions herself head downward over its siphon. This is a tube through which the mussel draws in water containing particles of food and oxygen for breathing.

The female bitterling lays her eggs in the mussel's siphon. The male then discharges his milt (a fluid containing sperm) over the mouth of the siphon and it is taken in by the ingoing current to fertilize the eggs lying in the mussel's gill cavity. Bitterling eggs are relatively large for a fish and are elliptical in shape. Their unusual size is because there is no need to avoid predators, protection being provided by the mussel shell, while their shape is an adaptation to fit between mussel gill lamellae.

The eggs usually hatch after 2–3 weeks and the young are released from the mussel a couple of days later. The young fish benefit from the virtually impregnable fortress formed by the mussel's shell, and are aerated by the almost constant current of water drawn in through the siphon. They do not encumber their unusual foster parent, nor do they feed on the mussel's tissues, as has been suggested several times in the past. The young are instead nourished mainly by the remains of the yolk sac, which is still with them at hatching.

# BITTERLING

| | |
|---|---|
| CLASS | **Osteichthyes** |
| ORDER | **Cypriniformes** |
| FAMILY | **Cyprinidae** |
| GENUS AND SPECIES | ***Rhodeus sericeus*** |

LENGTH
**Up to about 3½ in. (9 cm)**

DISTINCTIVE FEATURES
**Slender, minnowlike body; silver flanks and belly. Nonbreeding: greenish brown back, with blue-green stripes along sides. Breeding: colors become stronger, including violet, blue, red, orange and yellow tones.**

DIET
**Small aquatic invertebrates, especially worms and midge larvae**

BREEDING
**Breeding season: April; hatching period: about 2–3 weeks; young released from mussel 2–3 days later**

LIFE SPAN
**Up to 3 years**

HABITAT
**Densely weeded rivers, streams and ponds**

DISTRIBUTION
**Asia Minor and Europe, except Scandinavia and southern Europe. Introduced to Bronx River, New York, and parts of Britain.**

STATUS
**Common in native and introduced ranges**

In order to lay her eggs, the female bitterling needs the twin stimuli of the sight of a mussel's shell and the feel against her body of the current entering its siphon. There may well be an excited male bitterling nearby, but the female will not lay if a mussel is not also present. If there is a mussel but no male, she will lay the eggs anyway, which will be infertile.

Strong males are territorial during the mating season. Clusters of mussels are clearly an important resource for bitterlings, and any male that can monopolize a supply of mussels will have good reproductive potential. The stronger males jealously defend patches of mussels against rivals. However, there is an uneven ratio of male to female bitterlings. Due to there being more males than females, weaker males without a mussel cluster of their own attempt "sneaky matings" by releasing sperm into mussels before and after oviposition by the females. There is a chance that the eggs will be fertilized by their sperm rather than by the sperm of the stronger males that females prefer.

A mussel will begin to close its shell at the slightest touch and were it to do so while the fish was laying its eggs, the end of the ovipositor would be tightly gripped and almost certainly damaged. The female bitterling appears to condition the mussel to the touch of her ovipositor by nudging its siphon repeatedly with her snout before the moment of laying. The egg-laying procedure itself is so quick that observers have differently interpreted what takes place. What is certain is that the female bitterling cannot lay her eggs anywhere else than in a freshwater mussel. Moreover, European bitterlings display a marked preference for particular types of freshwater mussel, the species varying according to the location.

## Give-and-take

The mussels also benefit from the bitterling. While the female fish is laying eggs, the mussel discharges its larvae. Known as glochidia, these already have a miniature bivalve shell with a few sharp teeth along each edge. The teeth form almost a pair of jaws by which a larva can grip a bitterling's fins or tail. Once they have taken hold, the bitterling's skin grows over and encysts each larva, which is carried by the fish for 3 months, feeding on the fish's body fluids, growing a new shell under the old one and finally dropping from its host as a perfectly formed mussel. This is a highly effective way for mussels to spread since they move slowly.

Freshwater mussels are not dependent on the bitterling for reproduction, however. In places where bitterling are absent, the mussels simply release glochidia into the water. Many of the mussel larvae sink to the bottom and die, but some drift among water plants and come to rest on the stems. A few of these larvae manage to cling to passing fish, enabling them to complete their development. But association with breeding bitterling is clearly advantageous for freshwater mussels because it greatly increases the overall survival rate of their larvae.

# BITTERN

*The American bittern stalks along the reedy margins of pools, streams and ditches, taking prey by surprise with a lightning strike of its powerful bill.*

THE LONG, DAGGERLIKE BILL of a bittern shows its link with the heron family, but the neck is shorter and thicker than that of the larger herons and the body is rather smaller. A subfamily of herons, bitterns are found worldwide. The Eurasian bittern, *Botaurus stellaris*, occurs in most of Europe and Asia and in parts of Africa. It is about 30 inches (76 cm) long and its plumage is brown mottled with black, with a white chin and black cap. The feathers down the front of the neck are elongated, forming a slight ruff. Other species of bittern are distributed over Europe, Asia, Africa, Australia and the Americas.

The American bittern, *B. lentiginosus*, is very similar to its European counterpart in both appearance and habits, but differs in having a prominent black streak on each side of the neck, no black cap and a generally more streaked plumage. On very rare occasions it crosses to Europe. There are two other large species of

bittern, both in the genus *Botaurus*, the pinnated bittern, *B. pinnatus*, of South America, and the Australian bittern, *B. poiciloptilus*.

There are also eight smaller species of bittern in the genus *Ixobrychus*, which are about half the size of the four species mentioned above, at 11–23 inches (27–58 cm) from head to tail. They include the least bittern, *I. exilis*, which occurs throughout much of the Americas, and its close relative, the little bittern, *I. minutus*, which is found from Europe across Asia to Australia and New Zealand, and in much of Africa. Several of the small bitterns are more colorful than the large, cryptically plumaged large bitterns.

## Mysterious marsh boomers

Even where common, bitterns are rarely seen, because they are elusive birds that spend most of their time in reed and sedge beds unwilling to venture out even when disturbed. Moreover, bitterns are most active at dusk. Usually they can be seen only when they move, walking slowly and deliberately. When at rest bitterns match their surroundings, no matter what posture they are in or what their background may be.

One habit that gives away the presence of American and Eurasian bitterns is the booming of the males. This unusual territorial call can be heard from February to June and resembles the sound made when blowing across the top of an empty bottle. It is not particularly loud but carries well and is audible over a radius of 3 miles (4.8 km). Ornithologists monitor bitterns by counting responses to prerecorded bittern calls in different locations. Exactly how the booms are produced is still not known. It was once believed that to produce the carrying power of the boom, a bittern inflated its lungs, buried its bill in the mud and blew out explosively. Recent observers suggest that in the breeding season the male's throat is specially modified so that it can be inflated to act as a resonating chamber to produce the boom. As the bittern draws in its breath, it holds its head horizontally and pushes its head and bill upward to boom.

## Powder-down

Members of the heron family have patches of powder-down on their bodies. These are small areas of downy feathers that crumble easily, disintegrating into powdery particles when rubbed. Bitterns have four powder-down patches, a pair on the breast and a pair on the rump. Their function is to provide an absorbent for removing dirt, such as the slime from eels.

## AMERICAN BITTERN

| | |
|---|---|
| CLASS | **Aves** |
| ORDER | **Ciconiiformes** |
| FAMILY | **Ardeidae** |
| GENUS AND SPECIES | ***Botaurus lentiginosus*** |

ALTERNATIVE NAME
**Bog-bull (archaic)**

WEIGHT
**Up to 4¼ lb. (2 kg)**

LENGTH
**Head to tail: 24–33 in. (60–85 cm);
wingspan: about 43 in. (1.1 m)**

DISTINCTIVE FEATURES
**Long, daggerlike bill; cryptic plumage,
mainly brown with black on neck and wings**

DIET
**Amphibians, fish and aquatic invertebrates;
occasionally snakes and small mammals**

BREEDING
**Age at first breeding: 1 year; breeding
season: April–July; number of eggs: usually 3
to 5; incubation period: 24 days; fledging
period: 14 days; breeding interval: 1 year**

LIFE SPAN
**Not known**

HABITAT
**Marshes, reed beds and wet meadows**

DISTRIBUTION
**North America, except northern Canada**

STATUS
**Uncommon**

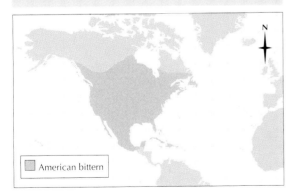

American bittern

The head is rubbed up and down the powder-down patches until it looks as if it has been covered in flour. This is left for a time, then brushed off by vigorous scratching with the feet. Finally the plumage is oiled with secretions from the oil gland at the base of the tail.

Like its relatives, the American bittern feeds on animals living in swamps and reed beds. Favorite foods include amphibians, fish and invertebrates, although crayfish, snakes and small mammals are also taken. Its hunting method resembles that used by herons: slow stalking through the water or waiting motionless with neck poised to whip out at passing prey. Victims are swallowed whole.

*If it feels threatened the Eurasian bittern appears to vanish by stretching its neck out vertically and pointing to the sky with its bill.*

### Secretive lifestyle

The female builds the nest deep inside a reed bed. Pieces of reed, sedge and other plants are loosely piled together on the matted roots of the reeds and made into a floating platform above the water. The female American bittern lays three to five dull, olive-brown eggs between April and July. She also undertakes all of the incubation, which lasts for about 3 weeks. After the chicks have hatched, she feeds them by regurgitating food from her crop into the nest. The young leave the nest after 2 weeks but are not fully independent until 8 weeks old.

A well-known habit of bitterns is that of "sky-pointing" with the neck when disturbed, so that the neck stripes make them hard to see against a background of reeds. Bitterns also turn the pupils of their eyes inward, which means that they are squinting under the vertically-held bill. The birds can in this way see with both eyes and thus measure the distance to the intruder.

Another reason for the infrequency with which bitterns are seen is that several species have become scarce. At fault is the drainage of wetlands to make way for farmland, habitat degradation due to water pollution, hunting and other forms of human disturbance.

# BLACK BEAR

**Three-quarters of the black bear's diet consist of tree shoots and other vegetable matter.**

color phases, including blue-black, chocolate brown, cinnamon brown and beige. The different color phases may even occur in the same litter of cubs. The black bear also has several subspecies, some of which have been given alternative names. For example, the creamy white subspecies found in a few areas of British Columbia is often known as the Kermode bear, and the bluish subspecies from the mountains of southeastern Alaska is known as the blue, or glacier, bear. In addition, the black bear is sometimes confused with another species of bear, the Asiatic black bear, *Ursus thibetanus*. For this reason, it is often called the American black bear.

## Great opportunists

Like most bears, black bears have an extremely varied, omnivorous diet. They feed mainly on insects, berries, nuts and shoots, supplementing this with the eggs and young of ground-nesting birds, rodents, fish and carrion. Black bears also hunt mammals up to the size of young deer and pronghorn antelope, and can tackle porcupines, killing them by flipping them over with their paws and attacking the soft underbelly. In national parks they are familiar with humans and beg food. On rare occasions they kill and eat farm livestock. Black bears have few natural predators of their own; old and sick adults are sometimes taken by pumas, and wintering bears may be attacked by gray wolves.

Black bears are good tree-climbers, powerful, quick to react and harmless to people, except when provoked, cornered or injured. They are solitary except during the breeding season, the two partners separating after mating, to wander far in search of food. The black bear sleeps through the winter after laying down fat by heavy autumn feeding. It does not feed during the winter although it may leave its den, a hollow tree or similar shelter, for brief excursions during mild spells. When startled, the adult gives a "woof;" otherwise it is silent.

Black bears mate in midsummer and the gestation period is about 220 days, including delayed implantation. The female's fertilized egg is not implanted in the uterus until October, by which time she is often in her winter den.

THE BLACK BEAR originally inhabited nearly all the wooded areas of North America from Central Mexico northward. Its numbers are now much reduced and it has been eliminated from large parts of its former range, but in national parks its numbers are increasing and elsewhere it survives close to human settlement. The black bear is up to 5 feet (1.5 m) long and weighs 200–595 pounds (90–270 kg). Its fur, claws and hind feet are shorter than in the brown bear.

As is often the case with animals named after their color, the name black bear can be misleading. The species in fact has a number of

# BLACK BEAR

| | |
|---|---|
| CLASS | **Mammalia** |
| ORDER | **Carnivora** |
| FAMILY | **Ursidae** |
| GENUS AND SPECIES | ***Ursus americanus*** |

ALTERNATIVE NAMES
**American black bear; Kermode bear; glacier bear; blue bear; Everglades bear**

WEIGHT
**Male: 255–595 lb. (115–270 kg); female: 200–310 lb. (92–140 kg)**

LENGTH
**Head and body: 60–70 in. (1.5–1.8 m); shoulder height: 36 in. (91 cm); tail: 5 in. (12 cm)**

DISTINCTIVE FEATURES
**Coloration highly variable, from all black to creamy white; muzzle usually pale brown**

DIET
**Very varied; includes fruits, berries, nuts, shoots, grasses, insects, fish, bird eggs and nestlings, small to medium-sized mammals and carrion**

BREEDING
**Age at first breeding: 5–6 years (male), 4–5 years (female); breeding season: June–mid July; number of young: usually 2 or 3; gestation period: about 220 days; breeding interval: 2–4 years**

LIFESPAN
**Up to 26 years**

HABITAT
**Forests and tundra; swamps, especially in Virginia and Florida**

DISTRIBUTION
**Alaska and Canada south to Mexico**

STATUS
**Population: 400,000 to 500,000**

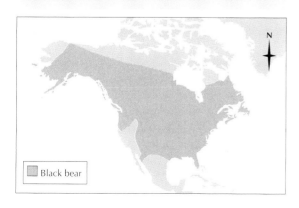

Black bear

True gestation then takes about 60–70 days, which means that the cubs are born in January or February. Usually there are two or three cubs in a litter, or exceptionally four or five.

At birth the cubs are 8 inches (20 cm) long and weigh 9–12 ounces (255–340 g). They are blind, toothless and naked except for scanty dark hair. The mother sleeps for another 2 months, having roused herself sufficiently to bite through the umbilical cords. The cubs alternately suckle and sleep during this time. They stay with the mother for at least 6 months.

## The original teddy bear

In 1902 President Theodore "Teddy" Roosevelt, who was a keen naturalist, captured a black bear cub on a hunting trip. He adopted the young bear as a pet. Morris Michton, a Brooklyn doll manufacturer, used this bear as model for the first "teddy bear," so named with the President's permission. The popularity of the teddy bear as a toy was immediate and worldwide.

*Black bears tend to follow regular paths through their home ranges, which are much larger in males.*

# BLACKBIRD

*Ornithologists consider the male blackbird to be one of the most accomplished songbirds in Europe.*

A COMMON AND WIDESPREAD member of the thrush family, the blackbird is found all over Europe, as well as in parts of North Africa, southern Asia and Australasia. The male has a glossy black plumage with a strongly contrasting yellowish-orange bill and ring around the eye. The female is umber-brown above and reddish-brown on the underparts, which have faint dark spots, and has a whitish throat. Her bill is mainly dark brown but may have some yellow on it. First-year juveniles resemble the hen but are lighter and more reddish, and the mottling of the underparts is more pronounced.

There are many unrelated species known as blackbirds in the Americas. Among the best-known are the red-winged blackbird, *Agelaius phoeniceus*, and the yellow-headed blackbird, *Xanthocephalus xanthocephalus*. American black-birds belong to the family Icteridae, which contains 104 species. Its members include such familiar birds as orioles, grackles and cowbirds. Their plumage is often largely black, but otherwise they have no affinity with the Eurasian blackbird.

## Nature's sentinel

Perhaps the most characteristic feature of the blackbird is its explosive, rattlelike alarm note, given whenever it detects a predator or intruder. It is often uttered in flight as the blackbird is flying to cover. The harsh call is also understood by other species of bird, which take the appropriate evasive action whenever they hear it. If a blackbird discovers a roosting owl or bird of prey it begins to call repeatedly in an agitated fashion, and other blackbirds take up the chorus. Eventually the disturbed predator may be forced to abandon its perch and move to somewhere more peaceful.

The blackbird is held by many to be among the finest avian singers in Europe. Its song is rich and flutelike, and is usually delivered from well up in a tree. The song can be heard from late February or March until early July, and is often performed at night.

## Familiar in gardens

The blackbird generally lives in one place all year round, although there is some short-distance migration, especially among juveniles. It is a bird of hedgerows, shrubberies and thickets, and is very common on farms and in woods and gardens. It thrives in suburban gardens, in part because food put out in birdfeeders reduces the normal winter toll of deaths. Short lawns also make ideal hunting grounds for earthworms, a major prey item of the blackbird.

Although the blackbird is often present in high population densities, it is rarely gregarious and communal roosts are the exception. Males in particular are aggressive toward one another at all times of the year. This behavior is much more pronounced in spring, when blackbirds run or fly in line, chasing one another.

Blackbirds are mainly insectivorous, feeding on insects and their grubs, earthworms, spiders, millipedes and small snails. A blackbird searches for its animal food by turning over leaf litter, mainly with the bill, sometimes with the feet. Seeds and grain are also eaten and berries and soft fruits become an important food resource in

# BLACKBIRD

| | |
|---|---|
| CLASS | **Aves** |
| ORDER | **Passeriformes** |
| FAMILY | **Turdidae** |
| GENUS AND SPECIES | *Turdus merula* |

ALTERNATIVE NAMES
**Eurasian blackbird; European blackbird**

WEIGHT
**2¾–4½ oz. (80–125 g)**

LENGTH
**Head to tail: 9½–9¾ in. (24–25 cm);
wingspan: 13⅓–15⅓ in. (34–39 cm)**

DISTINCTIVE FEATURES
**Stout, but not short, bill. Male: all black
with yellow-orange bill and eye-ring. Female
and juvenile: all brown with faint streaking;
whitish throat; brownish-yellow bill.**

DIET
**Mainly earthworms and other invertebrates;
also fruits and berries, especially in winter**

BREEDING
**Age at first breeding: 1 year; breeding
season: March–September; number of eggs:
3 to 5; number of broods: usually 2 or 3;
incubation period: 10–19 days; fledging
period: 10–19 days; breeding interval:
up to 4 broods per year**

LIFE SPAN
**Up to 20 years, typically much less**

HABITAT
**Forest, farmland with scattered trees,
orchards, hedgerows, parks and gardens**

DISTRIBUTION
**Most of Europe, northwestern Africa,
southeastern China and parts of India.
Introduced to Australia and New Zealand.**

STATUS
**Very common**

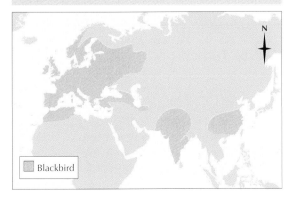

Blackbird

the fall and winter. At times blackbirds can be very destructive among strawberries and currant and gooseberry bushes.

*Blackbirds, such as this female, gorge on berries during the fall and winter.*

## Prolific breeders

Blackbirds suffer a high mortality rate. Their many predators include sparrow hawks, owls and domestic cats. In the urban regions of Europe a high proportion of the birds killed on roads by traffic are blackbirds, probably because the species tends to fly fairly low over the ground to cover when disturbed. However, each breeding pair typically produces two or three broods of young in a single season. In ideal conditions a pair can raise up to five broods. Such a high reproductive rate counters the species' high death rate. Blackbirds are abundant; there is estimated to be over 10 million pairs in Europe alone.

The blackbird's nest is usually located a few feet above ground level in bushes, but may be on the ground itself or high up in trees. More often built by the hen alone, it is cup-shaped, of grass, leaves and roots, often with moss, cemented and lined with mud but with an inner lining of dry grass. A clutch numbers three to five eggs, which are bluish-green freckled with reddish-brown or boldly marked with red-brown and gray.

The first pairs of blackbirds begin to breed relatively early, in March, often before wintry weather is past. Breeding becomes more general in April. Normally the season is over in July, after two or three broods, but exceptionally there may be five broods, the last in late summer. Incubation is by the hen alone and lasts about 2 weeks. The young, as nestlings and as fledglings out of the nest, are fed by both parents, mainly with earthworms. Juveniles soon disperse to find territories of their own.

# BLACKBUCK

*The horns of young male blackbuck are relatively straight at first, becoming tightly twisted as the buck grows older.*

ALSO KNOWN AS THE Indian antelope, the blackbuck is on average 47 inches (1.2 m) long, 30 inches (76 cm) at the shoulder and weighs up to 95 pounds (43 kg). It is one of the few antelopes in which the male differs from the female in coloration. The buck is a rich dark brown on the upperparts and the outsides of the legs, with white underparts and white around the eyes. In the doe the dark brown is replaced by yellowish-fawn.

Only the buck has horns and these are ringed and spirally twisted, reaching 28 inches (71 cm) in length. The narrow, sheeplike muzzle is white. The tail is short and the hooves delicate and sharply pointed. Today the blackbuck is found in a few parts of Pakistan and in India from Kathiawar to Bengal, including the Punjab, and southward to Cape Comorin. It has also been introduced to Texas and Argentina.

## Fastest on the Indian plains

The typical habitat of blackbuck is flat, open plains. They find shade in which to rest during the heat of the day, but otherwise spend their time cropping grasses and eating cereal crops where available. This sometimes brings black-buck into conflict with farmers.

Blackbuck are extremely swift, one of the fastest of all terrestrial animals, credited with speeds of as much as 50 mph (80 km/h). They can outrun the fastest greyhound and take strides of 19–22 feet (6–7 m) between hoofprints. When alarmed, one blackbuck will leap more than 6 feet (1.8 m) into the air quickly followed by the others, rather like its African relatives the impala, *Aepyceros melampus*, and springbok, *Antidorcas marsupialis*. This bounding is contin-ued for a while, after which the herd settles down to a steady gallop.

## Massive population declines

Blackbuck used to be the most abundant hoofed mammal on the Indian subcontinent and must have existed in vast numbers. As recently as the early 1900s the English naturalist and geologist Richard Lydekker was writing of herds of hundreds or even thousands. Today the species survives only in small herds in reserves and is scarce elsewhere. Hunting is the main cause of the dramatic fall in numbers.

Blackbuck usually occur in herds of up to 50, and herds of several hundred are now rarely recorded. Each of the small herds is attended by a single adult buck, which serves a harem of

# BLACKBUCK

| | |
|---|---|
| CLASS | **Mammalia** |
| ORDER | **Artiodactyla** |
| FAMILY | **Bovidae** |
| GENUS AND SPECIES | ***Antilope cervicapra*** |

ALTERNATIVE NAME
**Indian antelope**

WEIGHT
**71–95 lb. (32–43 kg)**

LENGTH
**Head and body: 47 in. (1.2 m);
shoulder height: 29–33 in. (74–84 cm)**

DISTINCTIVE FEATURES
**Male: long, spirally twisted horns; dark
brown with white underparts. Female: much
paler with yellowish-fawn upperparts.**

DIET
**Short grasses and cultivated cereals**

BREEDING
**Breeding season: all year, with peaks in
March–April and August–October; number
of young: 1; gestation period: 180 days**

LIFE SPAN
**Up to 18 years**

HABITAT
**Arid plains, scrub and dry deciduous forest**

DISTRIBUTION
**Highly fragmented range within India,
Nepal and India–Pakistan border region.**

STATUS
**Vulnerable. Population: 8,000.**

Blackbuck

males have a female coloration and short horns until they take possession of a harem, at which point their coats darken and their horns develop further. Interestingly, it is the does that alert the mixed-sex herds to danger.

At one time the traditional sport of princes and nobles was hunting blackbuck with cheetah. A 16th-century Mogul emperor, Akbar, is said to have kept 1,000 cheetahs for hunting. Each cheetah was taken hooded in an oxcart to where blackbuck were grazing. The hood was removed and the cheetah released. If the cheetah failed to catch up with a blackbuck in the first 100 yards (91 m) or so, it gave up and sat on its haunches, but should it make a kill, it was given a drink of the antelope's blood.

With the British occupation of India, shooting blackbuck became a favorite sport. Major F. G. Alexander, writing in 1911, told of shooting over 200 blackbuck as part of his hunting exploits, and many other British officers could have told of similar experiences. At the same time he indicated that poaching was rife. Local people used snares and organized drives in which beaters guided the antelopes toward hidden marksmen. The decline of the blackbuck and of a few other game animals may have been partly responsible for the virtual extinction of the cheetah in the wild in India.

## The legend of the unicorn

There is still some doubt about the identity of the animal on which the legend of the unicorn was based. Some name the rhinoceros, others the oryx, but there are those who suggest that it is the blackbuck. It is not uncommon for one of a blackbuck's horns to be deformed and curled like a ram's horn, or to be completely atrophied. This results in a one-horned, hoofed animal with a ringed horn similar to that of the legendary unicorn of heraldry.

*Most antelope are
swift runners, but the
blackbuck deserves
special mention as
one of the fastest
land animals of all.*

does of breeding age. The buck drives all rival males away from his harem. When the herd's young males reach sexual maturity, the dominant buck chases them from the herd, too, and they live for a while in bachelor groups before each acquires his own harem. Young

# BLACK-FOOTED FERRET

*Very few black-footed ferrets were left in North America by the 1980s. However, a radical conservation program now seems to have averted the species' extinction.*

THE BLACK-FOOTED FERRET IS the only ferret native to North America. The ferrets commonly kept as household pets are in fact domesticated individuals of two Old World species, the European polecat, *Mustelo putorius*, and the steppe polecat, *M. eversmanni*. Black-footed ferrets are also related to weasels, and like them are small carnivores. They have an elongated, sandy-colored body, short legs and black feet and a mask of dark fur across the eyes. In common with weasels, males are always larger than females.

Black-footed ferrets once inhabited the prairies of western North America, from southern Alberta and Saskatchewan in Canada south to Arizona, New Mexico and Texas. They also lived in the Rocky Mountains up to an altitude of 10,000 feet (3,050 m). The ferrets virtually depended on prairie dogs as a food source.

Before Europeans settled the great plains of the western United States and Canada, vast prairie dog towns were a common sight. However, as land was swallowed up by agriculture, prairie dogs were gassed and killed by the million. Black-footed ferrets are highly specialized predators and were unable to adapt their diet to this loss. Moreover, when the prairie dog towns were destroyed the ferrets lost their only source of shelter and cover. Ferret populations were decimated. Today the species' future depends on the success of captive-breeding and reintroduction programs.

## Desperate measures

The black-footed ferret was first described in 1851 by the naturalists John James Audubon and John Bachman. Only a few specimens have since been collected for study. The first scientific ecological studies of the black-footed ferret were not conducted until the 1960s. By the mid-1970s all the ferrets held in captivity had died and none had been seen in the wild for some time. The species was presumed to be extinct. Then, in 1981, a domestic dog killed a black-footed ferret near the town of Meeteetse, in Wyoming. A subsequent search found a population of approximately 128 ferrets living in the wild.

Over the next few years diseases, particularly canine distemper and plague, reduced the species' population to about 20 individuals by 1986. At this point a radical decision was taken by the conservation authorities. All remaining black-footed ferrets were captured and taken into captivity; in other words, the species was deliberately made extinct in the wild. Previous captive-breeding attempts had failed, but it was hoped that new technology and expertise would allow these animals to be the basis for a large enough population to support future reintroductions to the wild.

## Back from the brink

The gamble paid off, and in the first year of the program two litters of black-footed ferrets were born in captivity. In 1988, 13 litters were born with a total of 34 young, or kits, effectively doubling the global population of the species. The captive-breeding program was then reorganized into several sites so that if disease struck again,

# BLACK-FOOTED FERRET

| | |
|---|---|
| CLASS | **Mammalia** |
| ORDER | **Carnivora** |
| FAMILY | **Mustelidae** |
| GENUS AND SPECIES | ***Mustela nigripes*** |

WEIGHT
**1¾–2½ lb. (0.8–1.1 kg)**

LENGTH
**Head and body: 14¾–22 in. (37–56 cm); tail: 4½–5½ in. (11–14 cm)**

DISTINCTIVE FEATURES
**Lithe, elongated body; short feet; sandy coat with black feet and dark mask across eyes**

DIET
**Small mammals, especially prairie dogs**

BREEDING
**Age at first breeding: 1 year; breeding season: March–April; number of young: usually 3; gestation period: not known**

LIFE SPAN
**Up to 12 years**

HABITAT
**Short-grass prairie**

DISTRIBUTION
**Extinct in former range. Reintroduced to very restricted area of Wyoming and to single sites in Arizona, Montana and South Dakota. Future reintroductions planned in Colorado and Utah.**

STATUS
**Endangered**

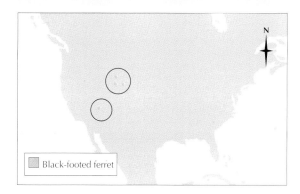
Black-footed ferret

black-footed ferrets have been reintroduced into the wild at sites in Wyoming, Montana, South Dakota and Arizona. The released ferrets have established territories in the wild and several breeding successes have been reported. Further reintroductions are planned in these four states and new reintroduction sites are also planned in Utah and Colorado. The conservationists aim to establish a wild population of 1,500 black-footed ferrets at 10 or more sites throughout the western United States by the year 2010. For the moment, the future of the species is assured. Indeed, the program has become a model for the conservation of many other highly endangered species.

*Much conservation work still needs to be done if North America's only native ferret is to remain a part of prairie ecosystems.*

## Poorly known

Little is known of the natural breeding habits of the black-footed ferret, though its life history is probably similar to that of other ferrets and of polecats. It appears to be solitary apart from in the breeding season. Adults mate during March and April, and females produce up to six kits. The young stay below ground until July and are able to breed at one year. Burrows offer an escape route from the ferrets' main predators, coyotes and birds of prey.

the whole population would not be at risk. The program has gone from strength to strength and 400 black-footed ferrets now live in captivity.

Now that captive populations are well established, the next phase of the program has swung into action. Since 1991 more than 700

# BLACK-HEADED GULL

THE BLACK-HEADED GULL is common not only around shores, but also inland where it may be seen following plows or searching for scraps in towns. One of the smaller species of gull, it is distinguished from other gulls, in Britain and most of Europe at least, by the chocolate-brown hood on its head. Gulls with similar-looking hoods include the Mediterranean gull, *Larus melanocephalus*, and the laughing gull, *L. atricilla*, another common species that occurs right along the east coast of the United States.

Only mature black-headed gulls have the hood, and then only in the breeding season; the young birds having a mottled brown cap instead. Juveniles normally take 2 years to reach sexual maturity. In winter the hood disappears except for small dark patches on the sides of the head and just in front of the eyes.

Black-headed gulls are found over most of Europe and Asia. In Europe they are absent from northern Scandinavia and Russia and occur in the Mediterranean only during the winter. Some black-headed gulls undertake short migrations, moving south in winter, and occasionally they make longer journeys. Individuals have been recorded from Greenland and a small breeding

population now exists in eastern Canada. The species is a scarce, but regular visitor along the eastern seaboard of the United States and has even been recorded in Mexico.

## Adaptability explains success

Although often called seagulls, gulls normally live on coasts, rarely being found out to sea. Many species are now found inland, and this is particularly true of the black-headed gull. It is a versatile scavenger, and garbage dumps outside cities are providing many new opportunities for the birds to feed inland.

Black-headed gulls have a tremendously varied diet. Along shores they search for small marine animals and scraps by plunge-diving over shallow water, dropping on the water to immerse head and breast but never becoming completely submerged. The gulls paddle on wet sand or mud, marking time with their webbed feet to make worms come to the surface. Sand eels, shrimps, winkles and a variety of other shore animals form an important part of their diet. The gulls also congregate in harbors and follow returning fishing boats, waiting for the crew to throw scraps overboard.

*The black-headed gull eats almost anything and employs a wide range of feeding techniques. Such versatility has enabled it to take advantage of urbanization.*

# BLACK-HEADED GULL

| | |
|---|---|
| CLASS | **Aves** |
| ORDER | **Charadriiformes** |
| FAMILY | **Laridae** |
| GENUS AND SPECIES | ***Larus ridibundus*** |

ALTERNATIVE NAMES
**European gull; common gull**

WEIGHT
**7–14 oz. (200–400 g)**

LENGTH
**Head to tail: 13–14½ in. (34–37 cm); wingspan 39–43 in. (1–1.1 m)**

DISTINCTIVE FEATURES
**Blood-red bill and legs; head dark chocolate-colored in breeding season, white with black smudges at other times; pale gray upperparts; white underparts**

DIET
**Wide variety of marine, freshwater and terrestrial invertebrates, bird eggs and nestlings, rodents and other small mammals, scraps, human refuse and some plant matter**

BREEDING
**Age at first breeding: usually 2 years; breeding season: early April to July; number of eggs: usually 2 or 3; incubation period: about 23–26 days; fledging period: about 35 days; breeding interval: 1 year**

LIFE SPAN
**Usually up to 20 years**

HABITAT
**Marshes, lakes, reservoirs, rivers, farmland, parks and garbage dumps**

DISTRIBUTION
**Much of Europe and Asia; small population on east coast of Canada**

STATUS
**Abundant throughout most of range**

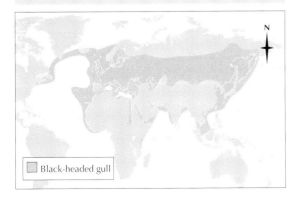

Black-headed gull

Inland, black-headed gulls feed mainly on human refuse and on insects and other invertebrates, particularly beetles and earthworms. They often hunt ants and other flying insects on the wing, and catch night-flying moths as they emerge in the evening. Black-headed gulls occasionally eat small birds and mice, and will also rob nests of eggs and nestlings, including those of other black-headed gulls. Coots and ducks are robbed of food as they surface from a dive, and shorebirds have their food snatched before they have time to swallow it. The gulls pester their victims until they are forced to regurgitate their catch in an effort to be left in peace. The gulls also include a small amount of plant matter in their diet, such as grasses, mosses, seaweed, cereal crops, potatoes and turnips.

*At the height of the summer breeding season colonies of black-headed gulls resound with the calls of hundreds or even thousands of birds.*

## Crowded colonies

Several thousand pairs of black-headed gulls may nest close together in one colony. Most nests are only 2–3 feet (60–90 cm) apart, giving the gulls just enough room to live without coming into conflict with their neighbors. Such colonial nesting is common in the gull family, Laridae.

In early March flocks of black-headed gulls congregate near their nesting sites, paying short visits during the day. These visits become gradually longer until the eggs are laid. The reason for this unwillingness to stay in the colony until eggs and chicks make doing so essential is that, sitting packed together, the gulls are easy prey for red foxes and other predators. A single fox can wreak havoc in a gull colony.

The black-headed gull's nest is usually made of grasses, but may be just a depression scraped in the ground. Egg-laying begins in early April in the North Sea area, but does not get under way until early June in Iceland and in other northern

*Black-headed gulls are now an everyday sight on park lakes across northern Europe.*

*L. marinus*, often search for their unattended eggs and nestlings. Mammals also invade the colonies and their forays can be traced by the remains of adult gulls, nestlings and empty egg shells.

Foxes are particularly dangerous to black-headed gulls, especially on dark nights when the birds cannot see their attackers. A fox may kill more black-headed gulls than it can eat, leaving some corpses unmutilated and burying others. Hedgehogs present no danger to adult gulls, but forage through the colony breaking eggs and sucking their contents. They also kill and eat young chicks. The chicks' reaction to danger is simply to freeze. This causes some predators to overlook them but is a poor form of defense against a hedgehog, which hunts by smell.

The reactions of adult black-headed gulls to these enemies depends on how much danger they present to the birds themselves. Hedgehogs and crows do not attack adult gulls and are therefore subjected to dive-bombing attacks, during which the gulls sometimes strike out with their feet. Foxes, on the other hand, are treated with more respect. The gulls hover over them uttering alarm calls and only occasionally swooping past in dive-bomb attacks, which are not pressed home. Black-headed gulls also defecate from a great height on intruders.

## Bird commuters

In the urban areas of northwestern Europe, some commuters may have noticed that there is another animal commuting with them: the black-headed gull. Every morning and evening flocks of gulls can be seen flying leisurely over the suburbs of many towns and cities. In the morning they fly into the center to feed. Parks, where people hand out offerings of bread to any birds willing to eat it, rivers, garbage dumps and playing fields all provide the gulls with food. Like house sparrows, *Passer domesticus*, and feral pigeons, *Columba livia*, which are properly known as rock doves, black-headed gulls have become efficient exploiters of humans. But it is garbage dumps that attract the biggest numbers.

In the evening the black-headed gulls move out of the towns and cities, returning to their roosts on lakes and reservoirs around the outskirts. Concentrations of 20,000 or more are known from reservoirs around London during the winter months. By banding the gulls it has been shown that each bird tends to go to the same area to feed every day and return to the same roost at night. In early spring most adult black-headed gulls return to their breeding colonies along coasts, but many of the nonbreeding birds remain in urban areas. It is only within the last 100 years or so that the species has been coming so far inland with such regularity.

regions. Each female lays three brown eggs with black spots and blotches. Sometimes four and rarely six are laid, but no more than three are likely to hatch because the gulls have only three brood patches. These are patches of bare skin on the breast, richly supplied with blood vessels, against which the eggs are placed to keep them warm. Both parents incubate the eggs, taking spells of several hours each.

The chicks hatch within 3 weeks, and can walk after a few hours. However, they do not go far from the nest at first. The parents bring food back to the nest and regurgitate it on to the ground for the chicks to peck at for themselves. The young learn to fly at 5 weeks, at which point they leave the colony to join the adults at their feeding grounds and communal roosts.

## Predators dive-bombed

Black-headed gulls have two types of predator. One attacks from the air, the other on the ground. Air attacks are usually made by crows, but also by hawks and other birds of prey. Black-headed gulls react to the latter threat by rising together in a dense flock and flying about with frequent changes of direction. This behavior works by hindering the predator's efforts to single out any one gull to attack. It is presented with a confusing mass of mobile targets, and usually leaves empty-handed.

Birds of prey do not usually take the eggs and chicks of black-headed gulls, although crows and several larger species of gull, such as herring gulls, *L. argentatus*, and great black-backed gulls,

# BLACK MOLLY

THE FISH KNOWN AS black mollies are in fact black varieties of several tooth-carps in the family Poeciliidae. The normal coloration of these fish is various shades of olive, green, brown and blue, with bands of bright spots on the body and fins, depending on the species. Individuals that are abnormally black to some degree occur naturally in three of the eight species of molly in the genus *Poecilia*. However, they are very rare in the wild. The entirely black forms referred to as black mollies have all been selectively bred by fish fanciers, and are popular aquarium fish.

Mollies are small fish, up to 5 inches (13 cm) long. They are characterized by having a large, rounded tail and a prominent dorsal fin, which in the male is larger and rather sail-like. The male sail-fin molly has an olive-brown back and pearly blue sides with bands of red, blue and greenish spots. The dorsal fin is pale blue and features rows of black spots and a yellowish border. The female is duller, with a shorter dorsal fin. The male wedge-face molly is of a similar color, but with several rows of orange dots and dark crossbars on its sides. The dorsal fin features black dots on its base, a black edge and a broad orange band. The female's dorsal fin is smaller and bluish.

Mollies are found in the southern United States, throughout Central America and in the Amazon basin in South America. The fish occur in both fresh water and brackish water, particularly near river mouths. Mollies are mainly vegetarian, feeding largely on algae, but also take small amounts of animal food, such as water fleas and mosquito larvae.

## Aggressive fin display

One interesting feature of mollies is their large dorsal fin, which is used by males in aggressive displays and in courtship. Rival males swim at each other with all fins expanded, but the fin display is essentially bluff, the contest being bloodless. The male displaying most actively or with the largest "sail" is usually able to intimidate his rival, and is most attractive to the watching female. During courtship the male comes over to the female with all sails set and, with fins quivering, takes up position across her path. At the same time the male displays colors as part of his courtship ritual.

In mollies the anal fin of the male is modified to form a gonopodium, with which he transfers sperm into the female's oviduct. The young develop inside the oviduct and are subsequently born alive. Several weeks usually pass between fertilization and birth, the length of time depending mainly on temperature. The young lie curled head to tail in the oviduct and are born one or two at a time.

## Color variation

There is a natural tendency in mollies toward the production of the black pigment, melanin, and occasionally "sports" (all-black fish) are produced. The aquarist takes advantage of this to breed black mollies. The black sports are obtained mainly from the sail-fin molly, less often from the sail-bearer molly and only occasionally from the wedge-face molly.

When the young black fish are born, they may be light or dark in tone. Most become light in a few weeks, and only begin to show black spots when about 1 inch (2.5 cm) long. Six months from birth some will have become entirely black. Others may not become black for 2 years, and some never do. One strain, the "permablack," is born black and remains so.

*The sail-bearer molly is one of the largest species of molly.*

*The Amazon molly is a naturally occuring hybrid produced when sail-fin and wedge-face mollies interbreed.*

## BLACK MOLLIES

| | |
|---|---|
| CLASS | **Osteichthyes** |
| ORDER | **Cyprinodontiformes** |
| FAMILY | **Poeciliidae** |
| GENUS | ***Poecilia*** |
| SPECIES | **8, including sail-bearer molly, *P. velifera*; sail-fin molly, *P. latipinna*; wedge-face molly, *P. sphenops*; and Amazon molly, *P. formosa*** |

ALTERNATIVE NAME
**Black molly**

LENGTH
**4–5 in. (10–13 cm)**

DISTINCTIVE FEATURES
**Prominent dorsal fin, sail-shaped in male; brownish, greenish and bluish, with metallic sheens and spots; all-black forms in captivity**

DIET
**Algae, small crustaceans and insect larvae**

BREEDING
**Number of young: 20 to 60**

HABITAT
**Freshwater and brackish lakes, lagoons, pools and streams, mainly in coastal regions**

DISTRIBUTION
***P. latipinna*: Carolina south through eastern U.S. to Mexico. *P. sphenops*: Texas south to Colombia and Venezuela. *P. velifera*: Yucatan Peninsula, southeastern Mexico.**

STATUS
**Abundant. Black forms very rare in wild.**

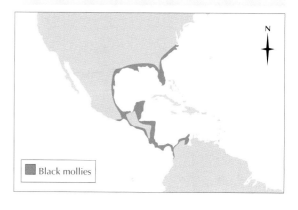

Black mollies

## Natural hybrids

The Amazon molly, *P. formosa*, is highly unusual in the vertebrate world in that it consists almost entirely of females. This species, which lives in the rivers of Texas and Mexico, is a natural hybrid resulting from a cross between *P. latipinna* and *P. sphenops*. The hybrid has characters intermediate between those of the two parents and is perpetuated in a quite unusual way. The hybrids are nearly all females, and they produce only female offspring. They cannot do so, however, unless a male *P. latipinna* or *P. sphenops* is present. This is because the Amazon molly's ova will not begin to develop unless triggered by the arrival of the sperm of one of these two species. However, the sperm does not contribute any of its chromosomes to the egg.

Thus, when a *formosa* female mates with a *latipinna* male, the progeny look like the mother in every respect. Similarly, when a *formosa* female mates with a *sphenops* male, all the progeny look like the mother. Perhaps once in every 10,000 young, a male *formosa* is born. Presumably it is able to mate, but so far there is no evidence as to whether the male Amazon molly contributes any genetic material to the offspring.

This extraordinary state of affairs is revealed by looking at populations of *P. formosa*. Mother and offspring look alike, behave alike and have the same internal anatomy. That they are truly alike can be tested by transplanting their tissues. Early attempts at transplanting hearts and kidneys in humans were unsuccessful because the patients' bodies rejected the alien tissues. Many experiments have been conducted on mollies, transplanting fins, heart and spleen from daughter to mother and between the progeny of a single mother, and there is never any rejection.

# BLACK WIDOW

THE NAME BLACK WIDOW is generally reserved for three spiders found in North America. However, it is also used for several other species in the same genus, *Latrodectus*, distributed over the warmer parts of the world. The North American black widows, in particular, are noted for their powerful venom, but the reputation is not entirely justified. The female of one of these species, *L. mactans*, is about ½ inches (13 mm) long. She is a shiny, velvety black, with a red, or sometimes yellow, hourglass-shaped marking on the underside of her almost spherical abdomen. The male, however, is much smaller.

The female's size and color have given rise to the alternative names of shoe button spider, red mark, red back and hourglass spider. The more familiar name of black widow is based on her color and on her reputation for eating her mate once he has fertilized her.

## Painful but rarely fatal

The female black widow spins a coarse, irregularly designed web, which often has a short funnel of silk, usually in the more elevated area. The male spins a similarly textured web, although his is smaller. Cool, dark places are chosen, usually in the countryside but sometimes in cellars, outbuildings and ruined houses and under doorsteps and porches. Although black widows are common, the number of people bitten by the spiders is surprisingly small. The known cases of injury or death in the United States for the period 1726–1943 total only 1,291, only 55 of which are known to have been fatal. That is, one death every 4 years and half a dozen injuries per year.

The evidence suggests that a high percentage of victims are children and elderly or sick people. It also seems likely that when death does occur, shock is a contributory factor if not the sole cause. The spider's poison is a neurotoxin that attacks the nervous system, causing symptoms such as severe headaches, nausea, sweating, fever, muscular cramps, paralysis and hypertension. The spider itself is retiring and more concerned with avoiding people than with attacking them. Moreover, only the females are troublesome as the male is too small to have sufficient venom to have any significant effect on humans.

*A female black widow, L. mactans, displaying the typical red, hourglass-shaped marking on her belly.*

With the exception of one family, all spiders have poison glands. These lie in the cephalothorax, the smaller and front portion of the two parts that make up a spider's body, and the poison passes through slender ducts to the fangs. In all but a few spiders, the black widow being one, the venom is effective only against insects and other small animals. It is introduced into their bodies by a stabbing action.

## Victims enshrouded in silk

As with other web-weaving spiders the black widow sits on the web with feet touching the silken strands. When an insect flies into the web and starts to struggle, the vibrations are detected through the feet of the spider, which immediately runs out and, by skillfully using its rear legs

*This female black widow,* L. hesperus, *is guarding one of her silken egg sacs. The several hundred young spiders that emerge from these cocoons will be almost identical to the parents.*

## BLACK WIDOWS

| | |
|---|---|
| PHYLUM | **Arthropoda** |
| CLASS | **Arachnida** |
| ORDER | **Araneae** |
| FAMILY | **Theridiidae** |
| GENUS | *Latrodectus* |
| SPECIES | **Several, including 3 North American species:** *L. mactans, L. variolus* **and** *L. hesperus* |

ALTERNATIVE NAMES
**Hourglass spider; shoe button spider; red mark; red back**

LENGTH
**Varies according to species; male has smaller body. Female *L. mactans* body: ⅓–⅔ in. (1–1.5 cm); leg span: 1¼–1½ in. (3–3.5 cm).**

DISTINCTIVE FEATURES
**Almost spherical abdomen. Dark brown to shiny black, typically with red (sometimes yellow), hourglass-shaped marking on underside of abdomen; male and young may be brighter.**

DIET
**Invertebrates**

BREEDING
**Number of egg sacs: usually 15; number of young: several hundred**

LIFE SPAN
**Up to 1–2 years (female)**

HABITAT
**Webs located in cool, shaded areas**

DISTRIBUTION
**Warm regions of Africa, North and South America, southern Europe and southwestern Asia; 3 species widespread in North America**

STATUS
**Several species common**

and quantities of the viscid silk from the spinnerets, quickly binds and secures it. Often it is only at this stage that the victim is stabbed with the fangs and paralyzed, subsequently to be almost completely enshrouded in silk.

Meanwhile a drop or two of digestive fluid is exuded from the spider's mouthparts into the insect's body, the contents of which are therefore digested externally. This process takes an hour or two, at the end of which the spider, by using its muscular stomach as a pump, sucks out the resulting "soup," leaving behind only the empty husk of its prey. This the spider finally cuts away and lets fall to the ground.

## Self-imposed widow

When adult, the male seeks a mate. He charges his palps, a pair of specially adapted appendages situated near the mouth and resembling short legs, with seminal fluid. During mating the male transfers sperm from the reservoir in each palp to the female's body. Only one mating is necessary for several bouts of egg-laying, since the female stores the sperm and uses it over a period, often of months. The eggs are laid in silken cocoons and the spiderlings hatching from them are, except in color and size, more or less replicas of the parents and independent from the start.

The male must approach the female very carefully. The approach involves a leg-stroking procedure and even the spinning of silk by the male over the female. In fact, when the female is too aggressive or has completed the mating she may break free from the male's silk and attack the suitor. The male, wary for his own well-being, may abandon both courtship and mating if a female proves to be overly aggressive.

It is popularly believed that female black widows invariably eat the male after mating. This, it is said, is the reason for naming these most venomous of spiders the black widows. Cannibalism certainly occurs, but not after every mating. Male black widows are polygamous, mating several times in succession with different females, and in zoos individual males have often been mated many times. It seems likely that following several matings the male becomes enfeebled, or indeed moribund. It is then that the female, taking advantage of the male's weakness, devours him, as she would any similar small animal that came her way.

# BLENNY

BLENNIES ARE MOSTLY small, shallow-water marine fish, although a few species live in freshwater habitats. They are most common in tropical and temperate seas, being particularly numerous on coral and in the shallows along rocky coasts. Blennies have slim, elongated bodies and lack scales on the head and body. They have two dorsal fins, the first of which, composed of slender spines, is continuous with the second. The anal fin is moderately long and the pair of pelvic fins located under the throat are each composed of two slender rays.

## In tune with the tides

Blennies survive each period of ebb tide by sheltering under stones or seaweed. The ease with which blennies can be found has made them favorites for study in aquaria. As long ago as 1877 a naturalist in southern England kept a species of blenny, the shanny, *Blennius pholis*, in a glass tank filled with seawater. He noticed that the fish became restless as the time of high tide approached. During the many months he kept the shanny, the naturalist found that it always knew the state of the tide.

In some places, such as the Mediterranean, tides are feeble or nonexistent. Blennies living in these areas have no need for a biological clock. Experiments similar to the one described above found that after a while captive fish behave as if they were living in a tideless zone.

With such small fish living on a rocky or stony bottom, observation of behavior at high tide is almost impossible. However, some idea of the blenny's habits can be gathered by watching fish in aquaria that approach as nearly as possible the blenny's natural environment. From such studies it is clear that once blennies are covered with water by the returning tide they become fully active.

## Aggressive behavior

Each blenny digs a shelter under a stone or rock, excavating the sand by wriggling its body. It may make several such shelters and will alternately come out to feed and dart back to shelter. The blenny moves over its home range, and grows uneasy if another blenny intrudes within a certain distance. Two blennies encountering one another will fight, butting with the head, biting, or merely raising their fins in a display of force. One fish will be dominant, the other subordinate.

The dominant individual always prevails, the subordinate retreats. In addition, dominant individuals actively eject subordinates from their shelters. Blennies also have favorite resting places on rocks, and these are determined by the same kind of pecking order, the dominant blenny driving away the subordinate fish.

In many species of blenny, the male is territorial during the breeding season. Thus, males of the species *Istiblennius enosimae* defend the area around their nesting sites, which are located in rocky crevices. The male blennies guard eggs left by the females, and any unguarded eggs soon succumb to predation and infection. The fanged blenny, *Meiacanthus atrodorsalis*, is unusual in that it has a venom apparatus, which is presumably used as a defense against predators.

The scale of dominance shown by blennies is largely determined by size. The more equal two blennies are in size, the more likely it is that a fight will develop between them. These fights do not amount to much: one fish may bite the other, inflicting only superficial wounds. Evidence of the blenny's nonaggressive behavior was demonstrated by two American scientists who kept blennies in an aquarium. The fish became tame enough to swim across the aquarium for food. When a cupped hand was lowered into the water, one of the blennies would come to rest in it. Soon the blenny would be driven out by another nibbling its tail. At times a continuous procession would result, each taking a turn to lie in the hand and then being driven out by the next.

*Most blennies live in the shallows on rocky coasts and coral reefs. The small proportions and elongated form of these fish enable them to shelter under stones and in tiny crevices.*

*Blennies are able to move their eyes independently, an ability that gives them an air of watchfulness. This adaptation may help blennies to avoid their many predators.*

## BLENNIES

| | |
|---|---|
| CLASS | **Osteichthyes** |
| ORDER | **Perciformes** |
| SUBORDER | **Bennioidei** |
| FAMILIES | **6, including Bleniidae** |
| GENUS | **127, including *Blennius* and *Hypsoblennius*** |
| SPECIES | **At least 730, including shanny, *Blennius pholis*; butterfly blenny, *B. ocellaris*; and black-headed blenny, *B. nigriceps*** |

WEIGHT
**Up to ¾ oz. (20 g)**

LENGTH
**Most species less than 6 in. (15 cm)**

DISTINCTIVE FEATURES
**Slim, elongated bodies lacking scales; 2 long, continuous dorsal fins; 2 pelvic fins under throat, each composed of 1 pair of slender rays**

DIET
**Small marine invertebrates, especially acorn barnacles**

BREEDING
**Age at first breeding: usually 2 years; breeding season: usually summer; number of eggs: up to several hundred**

LIFE SPAN
**Usually 2–3 years; larger species up to 5 years**

HABITAT
**Mainly shallow coastal waters, but some species at depths of up to 1,500 ft. (450 m); few species in fresh water**

DISTRIBUTION
**Almost worldwide, except in far north and in Arctic and Antarctic waters**

STATUS
**Many species common**

Little is known about the natural food sources of blennies. They are usually regarded as carnivorous or omnivorous. In aquaria blennies eat pieces of meat, worms and small crustaceans near the surface, so we can presume that their diet is wide. The shanny feeds on acorn barnacles, crushing the strong shells with its teeth.

## Male guards eggs

The blenny's oval or pear-shaped eggs are laid in empty mollusk shells, rock crevices and empty bottles lying on the seabed. The eggs are attached to the inner surfaces of such objects and guarded by the male or, rarely, by both parents. Some Caribbean relatives of the blennies, the kelpfishes of the family Elidinae, lay their eggs inside sponges. The young fish stay for a while inside the sponge, feeding on small plankton carried by water currents drawn in by the sponge.

The viviparous blenny, *Zoarces viviparus*, is not a true blenny but rather a blennylike fish. Also known as the eelpout, it belongs to the family Zoarcidae, most of whose members are viviparous (producing live young instead of eggs). The eggs hatch within the female's body about 3 weeks after fertilization but the young are not born until 4 months later. Each is 1½ inches (3 cm) long when born, and a single female 7–8 inches (18–20 cm) long may give birth to 20 to 40 young at a time. The largest females give birth to as many as 300 at once.

## Vulnerable at low tide

Blennies are most vulnerable at low tide, and more so when breeding, than when covered with water. Gulls take them, and so will rats scavenging the shore. Nevertheless, blennies are well camouflaged by their coloration and the mottled patterns on their bodies. Some, like the shanny, can change color to fit their background.

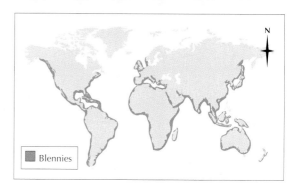

Blennies

# BLESBOK

Early settlers and travelers in South Africa recorded herds of thousands of blesbok on the high plains. However, the antelope were killed for food, to satisfy hunters and to make way for agriculture. This devastated their numbers.

Blesbok have soft coats that vary from reddish brown on the back to very dark and glossy on the rump. Around the base of the tail there is a patch of white, but this is not nearly so obvious as that of the closely related bontebok. A white blaze runs from the horns, between the eyes and over the muzzle to the nostrils. Between the eyes the blaze becomes constricted, and appears as two patches separated by a bar of brown hair. Calves lack this blaze. Their black foreheads and muzzles lighten as they grow older, become mottled within a year and white by the time they are mature.

Both sexes of blesbok have horns. Viewed from the front, the horns bend away from one another before straightening vertically and curving back over the neck. They can grow to 18 inches (45 cm) in length; those of females are more slender than those of males.

## Changing distribution

The original range of the blesbok was difficult to ascertain because of the species' similarity to the bontebok. Confusion was most evident in the south where the ranges of the two species met. It seems that in the later 19th century blesbok were to be found from the northern Karroo, through the Orange Free State and into the high veldt of the Transvaal, around Johannesburg. Blesbok survive in a greatly reduced range, Many now live a semiwild, or feral, existence on farms.

In 1962 blesbok were counted in some parts of South Africa. Nearly 9,000 were found in Cape Province, with 12,000 in the Orange Free State and 25,000 in the Transvaal. These numbers are far from those of the original populations, but with legal protection blesbok are no longer in danger of extinction. The current population is estimated to be 150,000.

## Life on the plains

The natural habitat of the blesbok is high, open ground where they used to graze short grasses, particularly red oat grass, *Themeda*. Blesbok

therefore do not seriously compete with cattle. Indeed, on farms cattle must first graze the long grass before the antelope can thrive on the shorter stems. During the dry season, however, blesbok are better able to survive the parched conditions than cattle. When water is accessible blesbok drink at least once a day, but they can go without water for several days if necessary.

Blesbok associate in mixed herds of males and females, although young bulls driven away by the strongest bulls may go on to form herds of their own. During the mating season the main herds split up, with each mature male separating off a small number of females and guarding them against other males. Rutting starts in April and continues for 2 months.

*Blesbok horns resemble enlarged gazelle horns. They are described as "lyrate," after their lyrelike appearance.*

*Young blesbok are pale in color. Over time, the coat darkens while the bridge of the nose and the base of the tail become white.*

The single calves are born from November to February. Females are sexually mature at 18 months, males later.

Lions and leopards were once major predators of the blesbok. However, now that most blesbok are semidomesticated and live on farms far from lion country, jackals are the major threat. Some calves are taken, although adult blesbok are more than a match for jackals.

## Domestication

Over the last 40 years there have been many projects in Africa to farm wild animals. There are many reasons for preferring the native hoofed species to domestic cattle, sheep and goats. The main one is that native animals are perfectly adapted to the habitat in which they evolved. They do not suffer from the diseases that trouble imported stock, and they are better able to utilize the rough herbage than domesticated animals from temperate regions, which need high quality pasture to survive. Native animals are also less dependent on a good water supply.

Blesbok are usually raised on ranches together with cattle, although the two are kept apart to avoid conflict. Unlike some of their relatives, such as klipspringer, *Oreotragus oreotragus*, and beira antelope, *Dorcatragus megalotis*, blesbok are not good at leaping. A fence 4½ feet (1.4 m) high is sufficient to retain stock. It is more important to fix strands of wire near the ground to prevent blesbok from crawling underneath.

There have also been experiments at keeping blesbok on arable farms. The blesbok are confined to high ground and allowed down into maize fields only after the harvest, enabling the

---

## BLESBOK

| | |
|---|---|
| CLASS | **Mammalia** |
| ORDER | **Artiodactyla** |
| FAMILY | **Bovidae** |
| GENUS AND SPECIES | ***Damaliscus phillipsii*** |

**WEIGHT**
**Male: 160–195 lb. (73–88 kg); female: 140–170 lb. (63–78 kg)**

**LENGTH**
**Head and body: 55–63 in. (1.4–1.6 m); shoulder height: 33–40 in. (0.8–1 m)**

**DISTINCTIVE FEATURES**
**Compact body and short neck; horns like enlarged gazelle horns; white face patches**

**DIET**
**Mostly grasses, especially red oat grass**

**BREEDING**
**Age at first breeding: 2 years; breeding season: April–June; gestation period: 225–240 days; number of young: 1**

**LIFE SPAN**
**Up to 17 years**

**HABITAT**
**Upland plains, including high veldt**

**DISTRIBUTION**
**Southeastern Africa, from central South Africa and Lesotho east to Swaziland**

**STATUS**
**Dependent on conservation programs**

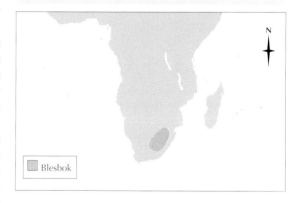

Blesbok

---

antelopes to supplement their winter diet with stubble and spilled grains. Keeping two species of stock animal on the same piece of land clearly has its advantages. The ground yields extra profit without requiring additional investment to improve its fertility. It may be possible to further improve productivity by introducing browsing animals that feed on shrubs.

# BLOWFLY

BLOWFLIES is a collective term for the bluebottles and greenbottles that are so unpopular in the kitchen. Their form is very similar to that of the housefly, but they are generally larger and their bodies have a metallic blue or green sheen. Other flies also have a green sheen to their bodies, however, and can be confused with blowflies. There are about 1,200 species of blowfly worldwide.

Blowflies are named after the condition of rotting animal carcasses which the flies infest with their maggots (larvae). The bloated state of the carcasses gave rise to the name blowfly. It was once thought that the name had Old English origins, as decaying flesh containing maggots was formerly known as fly-blown meat and flies depositing eggs were said to be "blowing."

## Detecting food

Blowflies feed on the liquids of putrefying food and carrion or on nectar obtained from flowers. They suck these fluids up through a moplike, flexible tube, or proboscis, which is formed from their mouthparts. There are organs of taste both on the tip of the proboscis and on the fly's tarsi, or feet. If a blowfly walks across something edible, it will automatically feed. Experiments have shown that if a blowfly is gently lowered onto a pad impregnated with sugar solution, its proboscis uncoils and starts probing for food as soon as its legs touch the pad.

When a blowfly finds food, it begins searching in circles, and the more food it finds, the tighter its circling becomes. This is instinctive behavior, enabling the blowfly to exploit food supplies to the maximum. If food is scarce the blowfly searches over a wide area, but when it finds a good source it stays to feed.

## Life cycle

The blowfly's life cycle is the same as that of most flies. Eggs are laid on suitable food, the larvae live on this food, pupate and finally emerge about 2 weeks later as short-lived adults. However, blowflies' life histories are varied, and some species lay their eggs in unusual places.

The female blowfly lays up to 600 eggs on carrion, where there is exposed flesh from a wound or in the eye sockets, mouth and other body openings of animals. Dung is also used. Some species of blowfly are considered pests by sheep farmers because they lay their eggs in

open sores and in the genital openings of ewes. Some blowfly larvae infest the tails of sheep, which is why lambs' tails are cut off. Blowflies are also a serious household pest. The familiar bluebottle buzzing around the kitchen is probably a female blowfly in search of meat on which to lay her eggs. Although they are a pest to humans, blowflies play an essential role in nature by decomposing dead tissue.

Normally blowfly eggs take a day to hatch and the larvae live for a week before pupating, when ¾ inches (2 cm) long. Blowflies are sometimes viviparous; this means that if egg-laying is delayed for some reason, such as the lack of a suitable laying place, the eggs remain in the adult female's body until they hatch and leave as larvae. Blowfly larvae are used as bait for many coarse fish. There are farms where blowfly larvae are bred in large numbers.

The maggots of blowflies are rather different from the caterpillars of butterflies and moths and from the larvae of insects such as aphids and assassin bugs. Blowfly maggots are little more than fleshy bags that eat and breathe. They have no legs and can move only by wriggling. However, the maggots have little need to move as they are surrounded by food, which is being liquefied by bacteria and by their enzymes, which are poured onto the food.

Before pupating, the blowfly larvae wriggle away from the flesh on which they have been feeding. The skin of the larva forms the pupa case and within it the body is almost completely broken down and rebuilt in the adult form. This

*Blowflies are often known as bluebottles or greenbottles because of their metallic coloration.*

takes about a week, and the adult forces its way out of the pupa case by sucking in air and doubling its size, which splits the case open. Adult blowflies live for about 2 weeks.

Some blowflies lay their eggs on healthy animals. One species, *Lucilia bufonivora*, lays its eggs on the eyes and in the nostrils of toads and frogs. The maggots penetrate the body and feed on the living tissues. The eggs of *Pollenia rudis* are laid in earth in the fall and the larvae invade the bodies of earthworms, where they hibernate. In the spring the larvae move along the earthworms' bodies, devouring their host's tissues. This species is found in North America, where the adult blowflies are called cluster flies or attic flies. They are a pest in the home, often gathering in large numbers at windows. The adults usually overwinter within the walls, attics and basements of houses and can enter the house through very small crevices in walls.

## Wounds heal quickly

During World War I doctors working in hospitals behind the entrenched armies found that the wounds of soldiers that had been unattended for several days and were infested with maggots often healed more quickly than wounds that had received immediate attention. Blowflies have a well-founded reputation for spreading infection, as they pick up bacteria and spread them by walking over food or regurgitating them in their saliva. Because blowflies routinely move between dead animals or dung and human habitats, they transmit diseases such as dysentery, typhus and cholera to people. It was surprising, then, that the unattended wounds healed so rapidly.

*Most blowflies lay their eggs on carrion. These maggots are feeding on the carcass of a dead crocodile.*

The doctors found that the maggots were eating the rotting flesh in the wounds so that the suppuration did not spread and the flesh could heal. This was before the days of penicillin and other antibiotic drugs, when slight wounds could become fatal. Consequently, blowfly maggots were bred in sterile conditions for the purpose of being placed inside suppurating human wounds.

## BLOWFLIES

| | |
|---|---|
| PHYLUM | **Arthropoda** |
| CLASS | **Insecta** |
| ORDER | **Diptera** |
| FAMILY | **Calliphoridae** |
| GENUS | **Various, including *Pollenia*, *Lucilia*, *Phormia* and *Calliphora*** |
| SPECIES | **Approximately 1,200, including *Pollenia rudis* and *Lucilia bufonivora*** |

ALTERNATIVE NAMES
**Bluebottle; greenbottle; cluster fly; attic fly; screwworm fly**

LENGTH
**⅓–⅔ in. (7–16 mm)**

DISTINCTIVE FEATURES
**Adult: larger than housefly; robust body; wide head; often has metallic blue or green sheen**

DIET
**Primarily scavengers. Adult: mainly flower nectar, plant sap and other sugary materials. Larva: decaying food, especially carrion; some species parasitic.**

BREEDING
**Breeding season: all year in warm regions, seasonal in cooler regions; number of eggs: up to 600; hatching period: several hours or days, some species bear live larvae; larval period: usually 7–21 days**

LIFE SPAN
**Adult: several weeks**

HABITAT
**Most terrestrial habitats, including woodlands, grasslands, meadows and within houses and other buildings**

DISTRIBUTION
**Found across almost every world region, including Arctic during its short summer**

STATUS
**Widespread and often abundant**

# BLUE BUTTERFLIES

The blues are a cosmopolitan group of butterflies, containing several hundred species. They belong to the family Lycaenidae, together with the coppers and hairstreaks. The pygmy blues, in the genus *Brephidium*, are the smallest butterflies in the United States, with a wingspan of ½ inches (13 mm). The long-tailed and short-tailed blues, which have short "tails" on the hind wings resembling those of hairstreaks, are commonly found throughout Europe and Africa.

The blue butterflies are named after the predominantly blue upper surfaces of the wings of adult males. However, some male blues are in fact whitish or brown in color, and in many species the females are wholly brown. The brown argus, *Aricia agestis*, of Europe, is an example of a brown-colored butterfly which is nevertheless a member of the blue butterfly family.

As in most butterflies, regardless of family, the blues have quite different colors and patterns on the undersides of their wings. Their wing-undersides are usually whitish and are often marked with orange or black spots.

## Life cycle

Female blue butterflies lay their eggs singly on leaves, or tucked into the flowers of plants. Some blues will lay eggs on a variety of different plants, known as food plants, whereas others are restricted to just one species. Vetches, trefoils and gorse are often used. The holly blue, *Celastrina argiolis*, lays its eggs on holly, dogwood and other shrubs, and the eggs lie dormant over the winter, hatching out in April.

When small, the caterpillars eat only the outer layers of the leaves or flowers, but later they are able to chew right through them and burrow down into the flower heads. In certain circumstances, some caterpillars eat others of their own species, devouring their fellows until only one is left on each flower head or leaf.

The caterpillars of the small blue, *Cupido minimus*, hibernate and retire as early as July. Having fed on the growing seed pods of the kidney vetch plant, each small blue caterpillar makes a shelter of a few flowers bound together with silk and hides there until the following spring, looking very much like the withered flowers around it. The pupa is formed usually on a leaf or stem, the caterpillar first anchoring itself

by a band of silk. Some emerge as adult butterflies within a few weeks, whereas others remain in the pupal stage for the duration of the winter and do not emerge until spring.

## Close relationship with ants

In many parts of the world, the caterpillars of blues have glands on the abdomen that secrete a sugary fluid called honeydew. This is rather like the honeydew made by aphids and, as is the case in that group of insects, the caterpillars' secretions attract the attentions of ants. The ants stimulate the sugar-rich secretion by caressing the caterpillars with their antennae and legs.

The presence of ants around the caterpillars no doubt protects the latter from predators, but the links between ant and caterpillar are in fact closer than this. The caterpillars of some species, such as the chalk-hill blue, *Lysandra coridon*, do not flourish unless there are ants present to milk them. Ants have been seen carrying caterpillars of this species and of the silver-studded blue, *Plebejus argus*, to the vicinity of their nests, placing them on the correct food plant.

## Foster parents

The large blue, *Maculinea arion*, of Europe and western Asia, enters into an even closer association with ants. In return for a regular supply of honeydew, ants allow the large blue caterpillars to prey on their own larvae. In fact, the butterfly seems to have become parasitic on

*The caterpillars of the silver-studded blue produce a sugary fluid called honeydew that is irresistible to ants.*

*The alcon large blue,
Maculinea alcon, is
found in much of
Europe but like many
blue butterflies is
becoming scarce.*

the ant and cannot survive without it. After its second molt the large blue caterpillar leaves the thyme flowers on which it has been feeding and becomes carnivorous, crawling across the ground until it is found by an ant. The ant walks around the caterpillar, then begins to caress it and drink the honeydew. The caterpillar hunches itself up. This is the signal for the ant to pick the caterpillar up with its jaws and carry it back to its nest. In two tropical species of blue butterfly, *Euliphera mirifica* and *E. leucyana*, the caterpillars will actually follow the trails of their host weaver ants back to the nest.

The large blue caterpillar is carried by the ant to an underground chamber, where it stays until development is complete. Here it settles down among the ant larvae, preying on them, and from time to time one of the worker ants visits the caterpillar to milk it. This is a departure from the ants' usual behavior, because normally they jealously guard their offspring, killing any intruder. It seems that the honeydew is important to the ants and that they are willing to sacrifice some of their larvae in order to obtain it.

Six weeks after being brought into the nest the large blue caterpillar, having grown rapidly, becomes fleshy, white and grublike. In the winter it hibernates, then completes its growth the next spring and pupates in May. Three weeks later it emerges as a butterfly and leaves the nest.

In many of the insects that associate with ants it is not the honeydew reward alone that prevents attack by host ants. The insects produce ant-mimicking odors so that soldier ants do not recognize them as foreign, and do not attack. Other species, such as *Arhopala madytus*, can

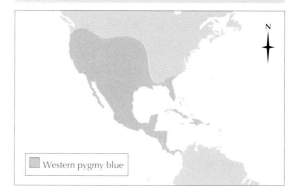
actually communicate with ants. They mollify the attack response in ants by mimicry, using stridulatory organs to produce vibrations.

## Blues under threat

Many blue butterflies are vanishing from areas where they were common, and a growing number are threatened. The intensification of farming and consequent loss of natural grasslands and wetlands is often to blame. In the United States the mission blue, *Plebejus icarioides missionensis*, of the San Francisco peninsula, and the El Segundo blue, *Euphilotes bernardino allyni*, of the Los Angeles sand dunes, are both endangered.

# BLUEFISH

*Bluefish move swiftly and appear suddenly in large shoals as long as 4–5 miles (6.5–8 km).*

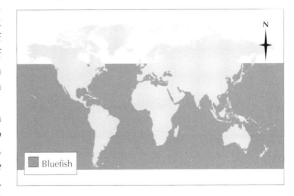

| BLUEFISH | |
|---|---|
| CLASS | **Osteichthyes** |
| ORDER | **Perciformes** |
| FAMILY | **Pomatomidae** |
| GENUS AND SPECIES | ***Pomatomus saltatrix*** |

WEIGHT
**Usually 1–4½ lb. (0.5–2 kg)**

LENGTH
**Usually 12–24 in. (30–60 cm)**

DISTINCTIVE FEATURES
**Dark bluish green above, silver below; black patch at base of pectoral fins**

DIET
**Menhaden, sardines and other smaller fish**

BREEDING
**Age at first breeding: probably 1 year; breeding season: varies across range; hatching period: 44–46 hours after laying**

LIFE SPAN
**Probably more than 10 years**

HABITAT
**Seas and oceans in top layer of deep water**

DISTRIBUTION
**Virtually worldwide in waters between 50° N and 50° S**

STATUS
**Abundant; population: hundreds of millions**

THE BLUEFISH IS remarkable for its voracity and has long been known as an important ocean predator. It is basslike in form and normally grows to about 15 inches (38 cm) long. Its body is bluish above and silvery below, and there is a black blotch at the base of each pectoral fin. The dorsal fin is in two parts, the spinous portion in front being the smaller.

The single species of bluefish occupies a family to itself. It is abundant and its range now seems to be extending. In 1991 about 14,575 tons (13,220 tonnes) of bluefish were landed in the United States, of which 75 percent were caught by recreational anglers.

## Ferocious predators

Bluefish attack many other fish with almost unparalleled ferocity. They cut fish to pieces and continue to do so until satiated. After an attack the trail of a shoal is marked by fragments of flesh and blood. Along the Atlantic coast of North America menhaden, *Brevortia tyrannus*, in particular are preyed on. Bluefish are in turn hunted by sharks and other large fish.

Bluefish are an epipelagic species, which means that they inhabit the upper layer of deep water. However, they may winter further down, at perhaps 300–600 feet (90–185 m), as they have been caught in trawls at these depths in winter. In summer bluefish sometimes enter estuaries when seasonally abundant offshore. Little is known of bluefish migrations, except that the species may travel considerable distances.

The eggs of bluefish are probably laid well out to sea and are likely to hatch after having floated to the surface waters. The newly hatched fish are about 2.5 millimeters long. At first the jaws and gills are nonfunctional, the eyes are without pigment and there are no pectoral fins, the young fish being dependent on their yolk sacs for a supply of food. Bluefish are probably able to breed when about a year old.

# BLUE WHALE

*A male blue whale diving off the coast of Mexico. Blue whales can stay submerged for up to 20 minutes.*

THE LARGEST ANIMAL that has ever lived, the blue whale can grow up to 72 feet (22 m) long and weigh as much as 150 tons (137 tonnes), the equivalent of 30 African elephants or 1,600 people. The average adult blue whale weighs just over 100 tons (91 tonnes). Only an aquatic animal is able to achieve such a vast size, because the water supports its immense bulk.

The blue whale is also known as the sulfur-bottom whale. This name refers to a yellowish film of microscopic plants, called diatoms, which is sometimes found on the animal's underside. Normally the species is slate blue except on the tips of the flippers.

## Ancestors lived on land

Blue whales belong to the suborder of baleen whales, or Mysticeti. Instead of teeth they have two sets of baleen (whalebone plates). These are made from modified hair, hang from the roof of the mouth and look like an internal mustache. Mysticeti is a name derived from the Greek word *mystax* ("mustache").

Together with the other baleen whales, blue whales evolved over 100 million years ago from primitive land mammals and became adapted to an aquatic life. Their nearest relatives belong to the ungulates, or hoofed mammals. Adult blue whales show no traces of external hind limbs, although they have retained some body hair and vestiges of the whale's land-mammal ancestry survive internally. The nostrils have migrated to the top of the head and are called the blowhole. In very young embryos the nostrils are in the normal mammalian position.

## Global travelers

During the summer blue whales live in the Arctic and Antarctic oceans, mainly in areas of floating ice. In winter they migrate to warmer seas, where their calves are born. The movements of blue whales depend largely on food availability. In polar seas there is a vast harvest of small marine creatures, but these tend to occur in patches.

Blue whales are usually solitary and associate in only small groups, although schools of 40 to 50 have sometimes been seen in the winter, probably as a result of small groups meeting and joining together. Like many other species of whales, blue whales come to the aid of their fellows in distress. Whalers know that if they encounter a pair of whales, it is best to shoot the female first because the male will not desert her and can be easily caught afterward. However, a female will desert a harpooned male and so be lost to the whalers.

Blue whales usually dive for periods of 10–20 minutes. The dives are preceded by about 5 minutes of blowing at the surface. The normal

# BLUE WHALE

| | |
|---|---|
| CLASS | **Mammalia** |
| ORDER | **Cetacea** |
| FAMILY | **Balaenopteridae** |
| GENUS AND SPECIES | ***Balaenoptera musculus*** |

ALTERNATIVE NAMES
**Sulfur-bottom whale; great northern rorqual**

WEIGHT
**Up to 150 tons (137 tonnes); fluctuates widely, heaviest in summer**

LENGTH
**Up to 69–72 ft. (21–22 m)**

DISTINCTIVE FEATURES
**Huge size; large ridge in front of blowhole; dorsal fin set well back**

DIET
**Krill**

BREEDING
**Age at first breeding: about 5 years; breeding season: May–June; gestation period: 11 months; number of young: 1; breeding interval: probably 2 years**

LIFE SPAN
**Probably up to 80–100 years**

HABITAT
**Oceans**

DISTRIBUTION
**Patchily distributed worldwide**

STATUS
**Endangered: Antarctic stock; vulnerable elsewhere. Population: 6,000 to 14,000.**

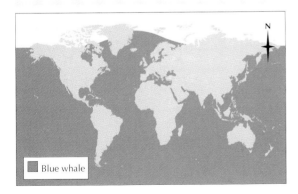

Blue whale

speed of blue whales is 8–10 knots (15–18 km/h), although they can sprint at speeds of up to 18 knots (33 km/h) if threatened. There are stories, many of which are doubtless legends, of harpooned whales towing whalers' catcher boats behind them.

## Sifting the seas

The rows of whalebone plates in the mouths of baleen whales act as sieves, straining off their food of small marine animals. The bulk of the whales' food is a 2-inch (5-cm) long, shrimplike animal called krill. To collect krill, a blue whale opens its mouth and sucks in water. The folds under the jaw and throat allow the floor of the mouth to drop down so that a large volume of water can enter. The mouth is then shut and the tongue raised, forcing water out through the baleen plates. Each plate is triangular, broad at the top and tapering to a point at the bottom. They are set ½ inches (1 cm) apart and the inside edge is frayed so that the tough hairs form a dense mat on which the krill is caught, to be pushed to the back of the mouth by the tongue and swallowed.

Krill exist in the largest concentrations at the surface of the sea, usually within the top 30 feet (9 m). Thus blue whales do not often have to dive very deeply for their food. Krill are also concentrated into certain areas by currents and temperature differences. They are densest in seas around South Georgia in the South Atlantic, where water coming through the Drake Passage mixes with water coming up from the Weddell Sea.

To supply energy to their huge bodies, blue whales must be voracious eaters. When cut open in whaling factories, their stomachs were regularly found to be crammed full of krill; one large individual had 2 tons (1.8 tonnes) of krill in its stomach. Occasionally a larger animal, such as a penguin, is consumed, having been engulfed while the whale was feeding on krill. How blue whales find krill in sufficient quantities remains something of a mystery. It is known that whales have an echolocation system similar to the sonar used in submarines. By comparison, in spite of

*Before diving blue whales usually spend about 5 minutes blowing at the surface.*

the advanced electronic equipment at their disposal, scientists have not yet been able to develop a system sensitive enough to detect krill.

## Migrations to give birth

When they are about 5 years old, female blue whales have their first calf. Mating takes place from May to June, and the single calf is born nearly 11 months later when the mother has migrated into warmer water. This is necessary because calves are born without a thick insulating layer of blubber. There is, however, less food in warmer waters and the mother must draw on the reserves of food built up while feeding in the Antarctic seas to sustain her at this time.

The calf weighs about 2¾ tons (2.5 tonnes) when born and doubles in length by the time it is weaned, at the age of 7 months. By this time the whales will have returned to the Antarctic, where food is plentiful, so the calf will find it relatively easy to learn to feed. As a female does not mate while she has a calf in attendance, she can breed only once every 2 years.

## Decimated by humans

Killer whales occasionally band together to attack blue whales, usually picking on young individuals. They tear chunks out of the blue whales' bodies, especially from the lips and fins and the bottom of the mouth, and even rip out the tongue. Only calves are likely to be killed, although adults may die from loss of blood. However, it was humans who brought the species to the brink of extinction, from which it has only recently partially returned.

In the 1930s there were an estimated 100,000 blue whales in the world's oceans. This figure had crashed to just 2,000 to 6,000 by the 1960s. In the intervening period the blue whale became the main target of floating whale factories and

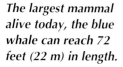

*The largest mammal alive today, the blue whale can reach 72 feet (22 m) in length.*

the associated high-speed catcher ships. Weight for weight, a single blue whale yields more blubber than other whales. As a result the species was pursued relentlessly, despite warnings from zoologists that too many were being killed. Today the blue whale is fully protected internationally, although whaling laws are hard to enforce in practice. Whalers now target more common species, but it is likely that some crews continue secretly to take a few blue whales.

## Wasteful harvest

It is appropriate to consider the concept of food pyramids when discussing the blue whale, which stands at the top of the marine Antarctic pyramid. The gigantic mammal converts krill into its own flesh, but the process of conversion is very inefficient. To increase its weight by 1 ton (0.9 tonnes), a blue whale must eat 10 tons (9 tonnes) of krill. Similarly, 1 ton of krill will have in turn eaten 10 tons of minute, floating plants, called phytoplankton. It follows that each ton of whale is effectively nourished by 100 tons (90 tonnes) of phytoplankton. This represents a loss of 90 percent at each stage in the pyramid. The food pyramid's inefficiency demonstrates how abundant life is in the Antarctic seas.

Only 10 percent of the energy supplied in an animal's food is used in building up its body; the rest is used in other processes of life, such as movement, keeping warm and reproduction. The low rate of conversion is fairly constant throughout the animal kingdom. In consequence humans could extract food more efficiently from the sea by cutting out one section of the food pyramid. Krill could be caught instead of whales; weight for weight, they are ten times more abundant. The krill could be processed into food for human consumption without the great loss at present sustained in keeping whales alive.

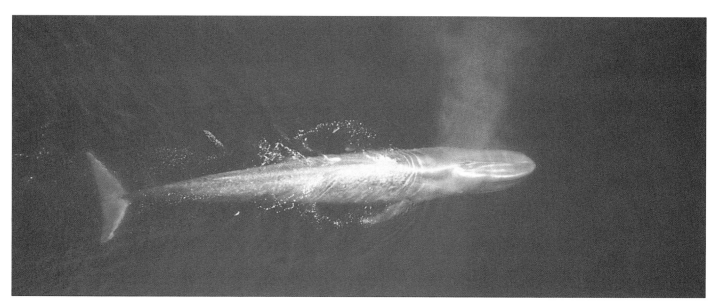

# BOA CONSTRICTOR

Some of the largest snakes in the world are in the family Boidae. The 39 species of boid are called boas in everyday language and none is so well known as the boa constrictor. It is not the largest of its family, being dwarfed by the anaconda. The sizes of most snakes have been exaggerated but there is a reliable record of a boa constrictor measuring 18½ feet (5.5 m). Specimens rarely exceed 15 feet (4.5 m), however, and large ones have become less common during the last 50 years, due to hunting.

The boa constrictor occurs in the warmest parts of the Americas, from northwest Mexico south almost to Argentina, as well as on Trinidad, Dominica, St. Lucia and several other Caribbean islands in the Lesser Antilles. Two species of boa are found in the United States. These are the rosy boa, *Lichanura trivirgata*, of the southwestern United States and northern Mexico, and the rubber boa, *Charina bottae*, which is found from British Columbia in Canada south as far as southern California.

Boa constrictors are cream colored, with brown markings in an oval or diamond pattern. This coloration helps to conceal the snake among sun-dappled branches. The boa's eyes are covered by a clear scale, so that it always appears to be awake. This apparent absence of blinking also aids in camouflage.

## Life in the trees
Unlike its relative the anaconda, which lives only near water, the boa constrictor is found in many types of country. In Mexico, for example, it is found in semiarid thorn scrub on the fringes of deserts, while in tropical South America boa constrictors live in dense, humid forests. Furthermore, the boa constrictor is largely arboreal (tree-dwelling); the anaconda does little climbing, although it sometimes basks in the sun on branches overhanging water. Crops and plantations are also a haunt of boa constrictors and they will visit villages in search of food, such as rats and chickens.

*Boa constrictors are mainly tree-dwelling. Their distinctive markings provide camouflage among sun-dappled branches.*

*Boa constrictors throw tight coils around their captured prey, causing death by suffocation. They then swallow the lifeless animals, such as this rat, headfirst.*

The boa constrictor is virtually harmless to humans, although the sighting of this snake near human habitation inevitably causes great alarm. Boa constrictors are not venomous and, like most animals, will flee at the approach of a human rather than stay and fight. Even if provoked into attacking, most boa constrictors are not large enough to kill humans by constriction, that is, by throwing a series of tight, strangulatory loops around the victim. In the rare event of an attack, a human can escape by running, for boa constrictors are not swift over the ground.

## Infrequent meals

The boa constrictor is nocturnal but has sometimes been seen hunting during the day. It feeds on a variety of animals. Most of the time the boa constrictor takes large lizards and birds. Only occasionally are larger mammals taken. For instance, a 30–40-pound (13.5–18-kg) ocelot was once found inside the stomach of a medium-sized specimen. Small rodents, including spiny rats, mice and squirrels, are the most common mammalian prey.

As boa constrictors are such slow-moving creatures, they cannot pursue highly mobile prey. Rather, they lie in wait or creep up stealthily on an unsuspecting animal. Less prey is caught using this method, but snakes need food only at lengthy intervals. When inactive, boa constrictors use little energy and can fast for long periods. Even when supplied with plenty of food, captive boa constrictors ignore much of it and eat little. Flesh-eating mammals of a similar weight must consume far more meat in the same period to stay alive.

The power of a boa constrictor's digestive juices is considerable, as is demonstrated by the fact that boa constrictors can feed on porcupines.

### BOA CONSTRICTOR

| | |
|---|---|
| CLASS | **Reptilia** |
| ORDER | **Squamata** |
| SUBORDER | **Serpentes** |
| FAMILY | **Boidae** |
| GENUS AND SPECIES | ***Boa constrictor*** |

ALTERNATIVE NAME
**Common boa**

LENGTH
**Up to 15 ft. (4.5 m)**

DISTINCTIVE FEATURES
**Large size; tiny spur on each side of body**

DIET
**Wide variety of small to medium-sized mammals; also birds, including fledglings and eggs, reptiles and amphibians**

BREEDING
**Breeding season: December–March (Trinidad), varies elsewhere; number of young: typically 20 to 60; gestation period: 150–240 days, depending on temperature**

LIFE SPAN
**20–30 years in captivity**

HABITAT
**Very varied, includes semiarid regions and tropical rain forest**

DISTRIBUTION
**Mexico south to southern Brazil, Paraguay and Bolivia; also some Caribbean islands**

STATUS
**Probably not threatened**

Boa constrictor

Only the hair and claws cannot be digested. A series of X-rays was once taken to investigate the digestive powers of a captive boa. A rat was held in the stomach for 4 days and the photographs showed that its bones were being dissolved by the snake's digestive juices.

## Clues to past history

Boa constrictors and pythons have a pair of spurs on either side of the cloaca, the genital and excretory opening. The spurs are present in both sexes, but are longer in the male and are the last outwardly visible remains of hind limbs. Vestigial organs in animals have often been found to have taken on a new function, and the hind limbs of the boa constrictor offer a case in point. From being locomotory organs, they have degenerated, and are now used to stimulate the female to mate by scratching her body, especially around the cloaca. Eventually the female raises her tail, enabling the male to wrap his tail round her, and mating takes place.

Were it not for boas and pythons the fossil record would have been the only direct evidence that the ancestors of snakes had limbs. In addition to the many lizardlike features of boas and pythons, these two groups of constrictor snakes actually possess the remains of a pelvis, or hipbone, as well as vestigial (imperfectly developed) hind legs, the spurs. In the boa constrictor the pelvis has the same number of bones as in lizards, but they are smaller and not joined to the backbone.

## Life cycle

Reproduction in boa constrictors is little known, despite the fact that they are commonly kept in captivity. The young are born alive, with an average length of 22 inches (55 cm) at birth. There are usually 20 to 60 young in each brood, though some boa constrictors have been known to produce up to 80 offspring. The young snakes may double their length in the first year, the rate of growth depending on temperature and food supply. Where conditions are favorable, some of the juveniles mature when 2–3 years old.

When young, boa constrictors have many predators, including jungle cats and predatory birds. As the snakes grow larger, however, fewer of these animals are able to overcome them. One of the boa's chief predators is the jungle racer, a snake-eating species of snake. The boa constrictor's natural reaction to danger is either to flee or to threaten by hissing, making a noise that sounds like escaping steam. This hissing can be heard up to 100 feet (30 m) away. The species defends itself by biting only as a last resort.

## Threatened boas

The boa constrictor has declined throughout its range, although it is not thought to be under threat. Several other species of boa are in danger, however, and the widely held fear of snakes means that boa conservation programs have been relatively slow to gain public backing. The Puerto Rican boa, *Epicrates inornatus*, occurs in humid forests and limestone country and is endemic to the island of Puerto Rico. It is threatened because large stretches of its habitat have been destroyed by deforestation and road construction. Another Caribbean boa, the Virgin Islands tree boa, *E. monensis granti*, has been seen only rarely since it was first described in 1933.

*Boa constrictors occur in many habitats and have a wide diet. Large boas have become scarce, however, due to habitat loss and human persecution.*

# BOAT-BILLED HERON

**BOAT-BILLED HERON**

| | |
|---|---|
| CLASS | **Aves** |
| ORDER | **Ciconiiformes** |
| FAMILY | **Cochleariidae** |
| GENUS AND SPECIES | ***Cochlearius cochlearius*** |

**WEIGHT**
**About 21 oz. (600 g)**

**LENGTH**
**Head to tail: 18–21 in. (45–53 cm)**

**DISTINCTIVE FEATURES**
**Very broad, flat bill; large eyes; black crown**

**DIET**
**Crustaceans and aquatic invertebrates**

**BREEDING**
**Age at first breeding: 1–2 years; breeding season: June–November; number of eggs: usually 2 to 4; incubation period: 23–28 days; fledging period: not known; breeding interval: 1 year**

**LIFE SPAN**
**Not known**

**HABITAT**
**Mangroves, swamps and riverside woodland**

**DISTRIBUTION**
**Mexico south to Argentina; Trinidad**

**STATUS**
**Not known**

*The boat-billed heron differs from all other herons in several respects. In recognition of its unique features, scientists have placed the species in a family of its own.*

THE BOAT-BILLED HERON is silvery gray overall, with black on the crown and upper back, a white forehead, throat and breast, and some rufous (red) on the undertail feathers and the center of the belly. The extraordinary black bill is almost as wide as the head. Observations have shown that the boat-billed heron uses it as a scoop, rather than a spear as in other herons. A short crest of black plumes sprouts from the rear of the head, but is often hidden.

The boat-billed heron is an extremely shy and elusive species. It lives in swamps with plenty of thick shrubbery and in woodland bordering freshwater lagoons and rivers. Coastal mangrove swamps are an ideal habitat. The heron hides in thick foliage by day, feeding on small aquatic prey under the cover of night. Strictly speaking, the boat-billed heron is not only nocturnal but also crepuscular (active at twilight), as much feeding takes place at dusk and dawn. Its very large eyes are an adaptation for hunting in low light.

## Secretive breeders

In midsummer male and female boat-billed herons form pairs and make a nesting platform of sticks deep in dense vegetation. The female lays a clutch of two to four white eggs. On hatching the nestlings have a short, triangular bill. The first, downy feathers are white on the underside and gray on the upperparts. Immature birds are cinnamon rufous on the upperparts and black on the top of the head.

In many birds and reptiles, the young hack their way out of the egg by means of an excrescence at the tip of the upper mandible, known as

Boat-billed heron

the egg tooth, which is shed soon after hatching. Eggs are highly resistant to pressure from the outside but readily broken from the inside. Perhaps the most unusual feature of the boat-billed heron is that the chick has not one but two egg teeth, one on the tip of each mandible.

# BOBCAT

AMONG THE VARIOUS species of cat found in the United States, including the puma and lynx, the bobcat is relatively small and comparable to the European wildcat. Bobcats weigh 9–34 pounds (4–15 kg) on average, though there is one record of a very large individual weighing 40 pounds (18 kg). The body is 26–41 inches (65–105 cm) long, with the short, thick tail accounting for about 6 inches (15 cm). The tail's stubbiness gives the bobcat its name, although the name probably also refers to the species' lolloping gait, which is reminiscent of a rabbit.

Body coloration varies considerably between the different races of bobcats, and is often linked with habitat. In general, the coat is a shade of brown spotted with gray or white, but buff-colored bobcats are common in desert country, and those from forest regions tend to be darker. The ears are tipped with pointed tufts of hair. Experiments suggest that these tufts improve the efficiency of the bobcat's ear in collecting sounds and that captive bobcats with clipped ear tufts do not respond so readily to sounds.

The bobcat is distinguishable from the closely related lynx by its lighter build, proportionately shorter legs, shorter tail and less prominent ear tufts. Lynx favor thick coniferous forest and tundra, whereas bobcats have less specialized habitat preferences. Bobcats occur in a wide variety of landscapes, including thick forest, open woodland, rocky deserts, scrub and even swamps.

## Natural loners

Bobcats are solitary animals that hunt mainly at night, and therefore they are not often seen. The size of their home range varies with the abundance of food and with their gender. Females maintain exclusive home ranges, and keep out neighboring females. The home ranges of male bobcats overlap. Males roam areas of 2½–40 square miles (6–105 sq km) while females range over 3½–17 square miles (9–45 sq km).

Bobcats leave several indications of their presence. The trails regularly used by bobcats can be traced, not only by footprints in mud, soft earth and snow but also by scratches on tree trunks where the cats have stretched and

sharpened their claws just as domestic cats do. They also have favorite spots for defecating and urinating, covering their feces and urine by scratching a mound of earth over them.

Bobcats are found in most areas of the United States, except for the Ohio Valley and the Upper Mississippi Valley. They are also found in southern Canada and in northern Mexico. The combination of small size, retiring habits and a varied diet has enabled bobcats to adapt to the spread of agriculture much more successfully than lynx. Indeed, farming can sometimes benefit bobcats by providing a ready supply of food in the form of calves and lambs.

## Versatile hunter

The wide range of food taken by bobcats is usually cited as a major reason for their continued abundance in areas where the face of the countryside has been greatly changed.

*The bobcat is distributed widely across the United States but, as a wary night hunter, is rarely seen.*

*Spots and flecks on the bobcat's coat break up its outline, helping it sneak up on prey unseen.*

## BOBCAT

| | |
|---|---|
| CLASS | **Mammalia** |
| ORDER | **Carnivora** |
| FAMILY | **Felidae** |
| GENUS AND SPECIES | ***Felis rufus*** |

WEIGHT
**9–34 lb. (4–15 kg)**

LENGTH
**Head and body: 26–41 in. (65–105 cm); shoulder height: 18–20 in. (45–50 cm)**

DISTINCTIVE FEATURES
**Short, stubby tail; black, tufted ears; coat variable, but usually has dark flecks**

DIET
**Mainly rabbits, rodents, bats and birds; also livestock, deer, snakes, insects and fruits**

BREEDING
**Age at first breeding: 2 years; breeding season: November–August; number of young: usually 2; gestation period: 60–70 days; breeding interval: usually 1 year**

LIFE SPAN
**Up to 32 years**

HABITAT
**Forests, mountains, semideserts and brushland; occasionally also swamps**

DISTRIBUTION
**Southern Canada south through most of U.S. to Mexico**

STATUS
**Fairly common; population: up to 1 million**

Rabbits, jack rabbits and rodents, such as deer mice, wood rats and squirrels, form the bulk of a bobcat's diet. Grouse, quail and other ground-dwelling birds are also eaten. Occasional food items include snakes, skunks, opossums, bats, grasshoppers and, very rarely, fruits.

Bobcats attack porcupines when there is a shortage of other food and porcupine quills have been found in bobcat feces, but the cats usually emerge second best in such an encounter. Bobcats with quills in their paws and mouths are likely to die of starvation, as a mouthful of quills makes eating impossible.

Bobcats are strong for their size and will attack and kill adult pronghorn antelope, deer, and livestock. The bobcat stalks its prey before leaping onto the animal's back, biting at the base of the victim's skull and tearing with its claws.

## Protected at last

Bobcats begin breeding at 2 years of age. Their young, or kits, may be born during any month of the year, but usually in late February or March. Twins are usual, although litters range in size from one to six kits and occasionally a bobcat will have two litters a year. The kits are blind for their first week. Breeding dens are located in caves, among rocks, under logs or even under barns and sheds. Females defend their young vigorously and fathers are kept well away until the kits are weaned, at which point they help the females to bring food for the young.

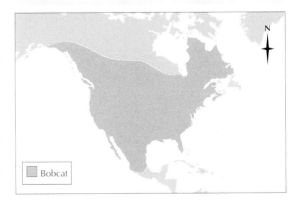

Young bobcats fall prey to foxes and great horned owls, but adults have only one natural predator, the puma. Humans have long hunted bobcats for their soft fur, for sport and because they kill livestock. However, 11 U.S. states have granted the species complete legal protection.

# BOLLWORM

Bollworms are the caterpillars of several species of moth. They attack the bolls, or seed pods, of a wide range of plants. Their name can be misleading because bollworms are insects, not worms, and do not feed exclusively on bolls, also attacking other plant tissues.

## Major pests

Perhaps the best-known species is the American bollworm, a serious pest of many agricultural crops and the worst pest of maize in the United States. The caterpillar of this species is mainly green and brown, with pale lines running along its back. The exact colors change as the caterpillar develops and may become brighter, even taking on a pinkish tinge. The adult is a small moth with pale brown and greenish forewings and paler underwings.

Another major pest is the cotton bollworm, an Old World species found in tropical and warm temperate regions. Its caterpillars feed on a variety of crops, including cotton, vegetables and ornamental plants. Caterpillars imported to colder regions in cargoes of tomatoes and other fresh vegetables rarely become a pest. They are not able to survive the winters in cold climates.

A third species is the pink bollworm, which was once estimated to be among the most destructive insects in the world. It is thought to be native to India, but now occurs in many cotton-producing countries, such as Egypt and Brazil, and in the southwestern United States. The caterpillars are ½ inches (13 mm) long and pinkish-white on the upper surface. The adult is a small moth measuring ¾ inches (2 cm) from wing tip to wing tip.

## Destructive life cycle

Caterpillars of the American bollworm appear to prefer maize as a food plant, but also devour tomatoes, beans, tobacco and many fruits. Depending on the crop it is attacking, the species is given various names, including corn earworm and tomato fruitworm. The adult moths feed on the nectar of many flowers, usually at dusk, but can be seen about on warm, cloudy days.

The eggs of the American bollworm are laid singly on the leaves and petals of the food plant, and one moth will lay an average of 1,000 to 1,500 eggs. Each one is shaped like two-thirds of a sphere and is ridged, resembling a minute sea

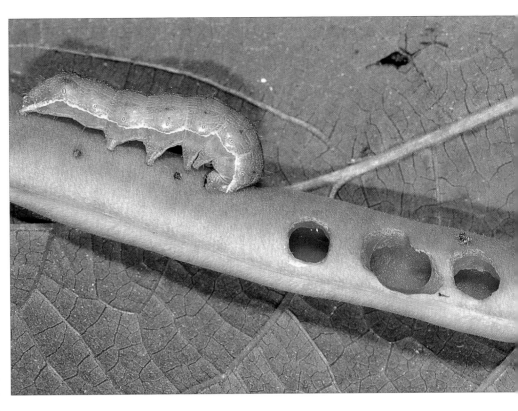

urchin, about half the size of a pinhead. The length of the hatching period depends on environmental factors, such as temperature, and the caterpillars immediately start eating leaves, petals and developing fruit.

Damage to crops is caused in several ways. Leaves and petals may wither and fall if eaten. Early in the season the blossoms may fail to open, and if the attack comes later, the fruits are made worthless, since the seeds are eaten. Where the fruits are destined for human consumption, worm infestation prevents them from being saleable. This is a serious problem for corn-growers; in the worst years over 90 percent of the ears in a crop are attacked and so made worthless.

When the caterpillars are full-grown, they crawl down the stem, or let go and drop to the ground, then burrow into the earth to a depth of 2–6 inches (5–15 cm) and pupate in smooth-walled cells. When the moth emerges from the pupa, it crawls back up the tunnel that was excavated by the caterpillar. There are three or four generations in a single year, rising to as many as 11 generations in the tropics.

## Hard to eradicate

It can prove very difficult to totally eradicate insect pests, and most pest controllers and farmers aim simply to reduce pest numbers to below the economic injury level, the level at which

*Bollworm caterpillars cause widespread damage to crops because they are highly mobile, eating their way throughout the food plants.*

## BOLLWORMS

PHYLUM **Arthropoda**

CLASS **Insecta**

ORDER **Lepidoptera**

FAMILY **Several, including Gelechiidae and Noctuidae**

GENUS ***Pectinophora* (in Gelechiidae); *Helicoverpa* (in Noctuidae); several others**

SPECIES **Several, including pink bollworm, *P. gossypiella*; American bollworm, *H. zea*; and cotton bollworm, *H. armigera***

ALTERNATIVE NAMES
*H. zea*: New World bollworm; corn earworm; tomato fruitworm; tomato grub

LENGTH
Adult wingspan: 1⅓–1⅔ in. (3.5–4 cm). Larva length: up to 1⅔ in. (4 cm).

DISTINCTIVE FEATURES
*H. zea* adult: pale brown and greenish forewings; pale underwings; dark bands on wing surfaces. *H. zea* larva: mainly brown and green, with pale lines along back; color changes during development.

DIET
Adult: flower nectar. Larva: more than 100 food plants, including maize, beans, tobacco, tomatoes and many fruits.

BREEDING
Number of eggs: up to 1,500; breeding interval: up to 11 generations per year

HABITAT
Wide range of agricultural crops

DISTRIBUTION
*H. zea*: Americas and Caribbean. *H. armigera*: widespread in warm regions of Old World. *H. gossypiella*: southwestern U.S. south to Mexico and Caribbean; also Brazil, Egypt and India.

STATUS
Abundant, but populations vary according to temperature and food availability

*The adults that emerge from bollworm pupae are moths which feed only on flower nectar. Although the moths are themselves harmless to crops, they will soon breed and produce the next generation of caterpillars.*

pests have little effect on crops. Farmers can also take measures to prevent the pests spreading, although this is more difficult now that transport is so rapid and goods are regularly shipped around the world.

This state of affairs is highlighted by the spread of the pink bollworm. In 1911 it was imported to Mexico in cargoes of cotton originating in Egypt. By 1917 the pink bollworm had already spread to Texas. Every year different pest species, including other bollworms, are found associated with traded goods.

Populations of bollworms can be kept down by deep plowing in the winter, which enables predators such as birds and rodents, as well as the weather, to destroy the resting caterpillars and pupae. The depredations of bollworms can also be reduced by early planting of crops so that the later generations of caterpillars do not have so much time to cause damage. Since World War II, DDT and other chemical insecticides have been used against bollworms, but once the insects have eaten into the bolls they are safe from many chemical treatments.

## Biological controls

Today many experiments are being undertaken to find biological controlling agents, that is, predatory animals that will keep pest numbers down. Ladybugs, for example, are voracious predators of aphids. Spiders may also prove to be suitable pest-control agents.

Another strategy, already being used in California against the pink bollworm, is genetic control. Sterile adult pink bollworm moths are released into agricultural areas. The sterile moths mate with other moths, but no offspring are produced. The release of sterile moths therefore reduces the reproductive potential of bollworms in a given area, with corresponding negative impacts on the size of bollworm populations. This method of control is controversial, but reduces the need for powerful insecticides.

# BOMBAY DUCK

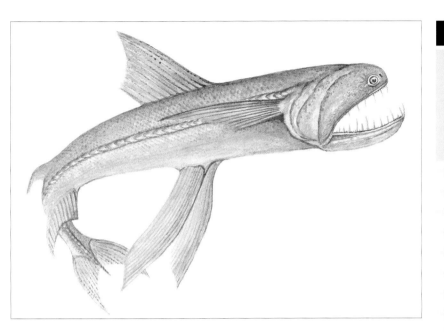

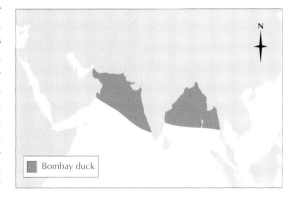

| BOMBAY DUCK | |
|---|---|
| CLASS | **Osteichthyes** |
| ORDER | **Aulopiformes** |
| FAMILY | **Synodontidae** |
| GENUS AND SPECIES | ***Harpedon nehereus*** |

ALTERNATIVE NAMES
**Bummalo; bummalaw**

LENGTH
**Up to 16 in. (41 cm)**

DISTINCTIVE FEATURES
**Long, slender body; large head; very long, heavily toothed jaws; long fins; covered with thin, transparent scales**

DIET
**Shrimps and small fish**

BREEDING
**Poorly known**

LIFE SPAN
**Probably less than 3 years**

HABITAT
**Warm seas; visits estuaries and low-salt waters near river mouths**

DISTRIBUTION
**Northern Indian Ocean, Bay of Bengal and Arabian Sea**

STATUS
**Abundant**

*It is commonly said that the Bombay duck glows with a brilliantly phosphorescent light when freshly caught, due to bacteria in its surface slime. Some experts, however, say that the fish has light organs, similar to those in deep-sea fish.*

THIS SPECIES WAS named the *bummalo*, or *bummalaw*, by Europeans in 1673. The name by which it is now known is an alteration of the Indian word *bombil*, a reference to the place name, Bombay. "Duck" is a fanciful addition.

The Bombay duck is a long, salmon-type fish with a maximum length of 16 inches (41 cm), though most of those caught are much smaller. The body is covered with thin, transparent scales. The paired fins are long, each pelvic fin having nine rays, and the tail fin has a third, small lobe.

## Mysterious movements

Knowledge of the Bombay duck is scanty and in some respects contradictory. The fish appears in large numbers off the coasts of India in the monsoon periods. It has been suggested that the species comes inshore at those times because a large volume of well-oxygenated water enters the sea from rivers swollen by the monsoon rains. The fresh water also carries large quantities of nutrient salts washed down from the soil of India's mountains and plains. This acts as a fertilizer for the millions of plankton floating and growing in the sunshine, near the sea's surface. The various species of animal plankton, including various shrimps, feed on the plant plankton, so there is a sudden increase in the Bombay duck's food supply.

What happens during the rest of the year is still unknown. The Bombay duck seems to be an oceanic species, migrating inshore for the rich feed and then returning. The fish itself is delicate and easily damaged in trawl nets, just as delicate deep-sea fishes are damaged. Its appearance, especially its large mouth and conspicuous barbed teeth, are also reminiscent of a deep-sea species. It is clear that the Bombay duck is a wandering fish. But whether its wanderings constitute a migration or are simply a sign of nomadic behavior has yet to be seen.

# BONITO

*Bonito change color when courting and when pursuing prey. The flanks develop dark vertical bars and a yellow stripe appears along the back. When bonito are caught, they display this pattern as a result of swimming at the bait.*

THE NAME BONITO IS applied to several species of the mackerel family. The one discussed here, *Sarda sarda*, is the most common. It is found on both sides of the Atlantic, mainly in tropical and subtropical waters, and occasionally in temperate regions. The fish is up to 30 inches (75 cm) long, steel-blue in color and shaped like a tuna, with a streamlined body and a series of finlets behind the dorsal and anal fins.

Bonito hunt smaller fish by sight, catching the prey head first. Their feeding behavior is also stimulated by chemicals released from the bodies of their prey. Young bonito are in turn hunted by predatory fish, including adult bonito, which are themselves taken by tuna and sharks.

## Sink or swim

Bonito have no gas-filled swim bladder to give them buoyancy, and are heavier than seawater. However, they can keep at a constant depth by cruising at about 2 miles per hour (3 km/h) with their pectoral fins spread. The planing action of the fins in the water gives the fish's body the necessary lift. Bonito swim with a closed mouth, which is opened at intervals to allow water to pass across the gills. They attain a top speed of 10 miles per hour (16 km/h), about half that of tuna.

## Wobbling courtship

During courtship the female bonito swims along a wobbling course with the male either swimming close behind her or in tight circles. The male may swim so close behind the female that his nose is touching her tail fins. The wobbling

| ATLANTIC BONITO | |
|---|---|
| CLASS | **Osteichthyes** |
| ORDER | **Perciformes** |
| FAMILY | **Scombridae** |
| GENUS AND SPECIES | ***Sarda sarda*** |

**WEIGHT**
**Up to 18 lb. (8 kg)**

**LENGTH**
**Up to 30 in. (75 cm)**

**DISTINCTIVE FEATURES**
**Long, streamlined body; dark bars on flanks and yellow midline on back appear at speed**

**DIET**
**Small fish**

**BREEDING**
**Age at first breeding: probably 1 year**

**LIFE SPAN**
**Probably up to 10 years**

**HABITAT**
**Top layer of oceans, over continental shelf**

**DISTRIBUTION**
**Tropical and temperate coasts of Atlantic, Mediterranean and Black Sea**

**STATUS**
**Population: tens or hundreds of millions**

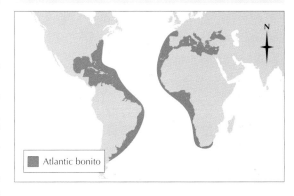

Atlantic bonito

action is triggered when a sexually excited male swims toward a female. If another male approaches the pair, the courting male will swim away from the female and align himself alongside the second male. There is no physical contact between the two rivals in such situations, but both fish show vertical dark bars and a yellow line along their backs.

# BONTEBOK

T HE BONTEBOK IS very closely related to another species of small antelope, the blesbok, which it resembles. Some authorities consider the bontebok and blesbok to be races of the same species because the two antelope interbreed in captivity. However, their offspring have not yet been shown to be fertile. This suggests that the bontebok and blesbok belong no more to the same species than do the domestic horse and ass, which produce the sterile mule.

Bontebok are a little larger than blesbok, standing over 39 inches (1 m) at the shoulder. They weigh up to 175 pounds (80 kg), similar to the weight of the blesbok. Bontebok horns grow to 15–16 inches (38–41 cm) and are the same shape as those of the blesbok. The white blaze on the face is complete, running from the tip of the nose to the base of the horns, whereas blesbok have a brown line between the eyes that divides the white patch in two. Bontebok also have a much more conspicuous white rump. The name bontebok means "pied," or "painted," buck, in recognition of the species' prominent markings on the face, rump and the insides of the legs.

## Saved from extinction
The bontebok was well known to the early Dutch settlers in South Africa as it is found in the lower coastal area of the Cape Province, the region first colonized south of the Orange River. These settlers did not discover the very similar blesbok, which lives on higher ground inland, on the plains of the Karroo and the high veldt of the Transvaal, until they trekked northward in the 19th century.

Being so accessible, the bontebok suffered from hunting far more than its higher-altitude relative. It would have been driven to extinction early in the 19th century had it not been for the efforts of a few farmers. Although a license from a magistrate was required to kill bontebok and a heavy fine was imposed on poachers, this only slowed down the process of extermination. The bontebok's extinction was averted by Alexander Van der Byl of Bredasdorp, who, when enclosing his farm, thought of driving the bontebok from the neighboring plain into the enclosure. About 30 antelope, a large proportion of the remaining population, were captured in this way. Some of Van der Byl's neighbors followed suit, and soon the only bontebok that existed outside these farms were the members of a few wild herds.

## Fleet of foot
When alarmed, bontebok run against the wind. They are very swift and are capable of great endurance. If pressed, the antelope run with their heads down and noses almost touching the grass. Bontebok calves at a week old can already outrun a horse.

*In the early 1800s the bontebok was hunted almost to extinction, but it survived to lead a semidomesticated existence on farms.*

*Although there are no longer any bontebok in the wild, they are not endangered. This herd is at the De Hoop Nature Reserve in Western Cape, South Africa.*

### BONTEBOK

| | |
|---|---|
| CLASS | **Mammalia** |
| ORDER | **Artiodactyla** |
| FAMILY | **Bovidae** |
| GENUS AND SPECIES | ***Damaliscus dorcas*** |

WEIGHT
**Male: 145–175 lb. (65–80 kg); female: 120–155 lb. (55–70 kg)**

LENGTH
**Head and body: 55–63 in. (1.4–1.6 m); shoulder height: 33–39 in. (0.8–1 m); tail: 12–18 in. (30–45 cm)**

DISTINCTIVE FEATURES
**Closely resembles blesbok, but with bolder white markings on face, rump and legs**

DIET
**Mainly grasses**

BREEDING
**Age at first breeding: 2 years; breeding season: April–June; gestation period: about 240 days; number of young: 1**

LIFE SPAN
**Up to 17 years**

HABITAT
**Lowland grasslands**

DISTRIBUTION
**Restricted to fenced land on nature reserves and farms in southwestern South Africa**

STATUS
**Vulnerable. Population: 1,500.**

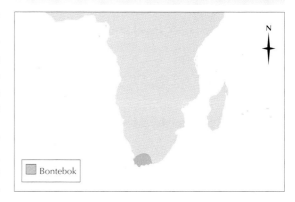

As with blesbok, lions and leopards were once the chief predators of bontebok, but the species is now mostly safe from these carnivores. Not only are lions and leopards rarer than they used to be, the few bontebok remaining are now kept in enclosures, such as at the Cape Point and Bontebok nature reserves.

## Populations become separate species

The bontebok was the common small antelope familiar to the Dutch Boer settlers around the Cape of Good Hope. The Boers had known the animal for 100 years when some of them started to move inland to find new areas in which to settle. As they moved up onto the open plains that were more suitable for cultivation than the lower, partly wooded areas, more antelope were seen. These antelope were little different from the antelope around the Cape and were, accordingly, also called bontebok. Some plains to the south of the Orange River are still known as bontebok flats.

In 1836 the Boers crossed the Orange River and came across many more of the antelope. The old settlers who had been born and bred in the country continued to call them bontebok, but the new settlers called them blesbok after the white blaze on the face.

There has been much confusion over precisely which animals the names bontebok and blesbok refer to. The situation is a good instance of the need for giving species unambiguous scientific names. There is confusion in even the Latin names of bontebok and blesbok because zoologists differ over whether these antelope are different species or different races of the same species. The pair are probably descended from a not-too-distant common ancestor. Two populations of this ancestor became separated, the one on lowland, the other on highland plains. The lowland population grazed mainly *Bromus* and *Danthonia* grasses, whereas the diet of the upland population consisted largely of *Themeda* and *Chloromelas* grasses. In isolation the antelope evolved adaptations to better suit their respective environments, resulting in the distinct forms we know today as the bontebok and blesbok.

# BOOBY

Booby is the name applied to six species of the gannet family that live mainly in tropical regions. The name comes from the Spanish word *bobo*, "dunce," and alludes to the birds' extreme clumsiness on land and to their lack of fear of humans.

Boobies are goose-sized birds, heavily built with thick necks and large heads. The bill is stout, broad at the base and tapering to a point; the wings are long and pointed. Like albatrosses, boobies walk awkwardly but are powerful and agile fliers. Boobies have webbed feet set as far back as possible at the rear of the belly, an ideal arrangement for swimming in the sea but not for movement on land.

## Wide-ranging species

Three species of booby are widespread in tropical regions, breeding on coasts and islands and feeding over the sea. The brown booby, *Sula leucogaster*, is the most common in many parts of the Tropics, and differs from the others in not having an almost wholly white body. Its upperparts are dark brown, providing a strong contrast with its white underparts. Around the bill and under the throat is a patch of bare skin, which is dark blue in males and yellow in females.

The red-footed booby, *S. sula*, is mainly white with black primary wing feathers and a gray-brown tail. The bare skin on its head is black and red. The remaining widespread species of booby is the masked, or blue-faced, booby, *S. dactylatra*. Its plumage is also mainly white and it has blue-black naked skin on the face and yellow or greenish feet.

## Localized species

The other three species of booby all have relatively restricted ranges. The Peruvian booby, or *piquero, S. variegata*, is the commonest seabird of the cool Humboldt Current that runs along the coast of Chile and Peru. The blue-footed booby, *S. nebouxii*, which has a distinctive mottled brown and white body and bright blue feet, also lives on the west coast of the Americas. However, it is confined to warmer waters from California to northern Peru. Abbott's booby, *S. abotti*, breeds only on Assumption Island and Christmas Island in the Indian Ocean.

## Plunge-divers

Boobies have a distinctive method of catching prey. Soaring perhaps 100 feet (30 m) above the sea, the birds partly close their wings and plummet down, crashing bill first into the water. The shock of the impact is cushioned by air sacs under the skin of the head, and damage to the brain is prevented by a specially strong skull. This spectacular display is used by all of the gannet family to catch fish and squid.

Once in the sea, boobies chase their prey by swimming both with wings and feet. Rather than catching victims by spearing them during

*Boobies, such as this masked booby, are superb swimmers but clumsy on land. Their webbed feet are set far back on the body to increase their power as paddles, and are thus poorly suited to walking.*

*A masked booby with its chick. Booby chicks hatch naked but within 2 weeks are covered with fluffy white down.*

## BROWN BOOBY

| | |
|---|---|
| CLASS | **Aves** |
| ORDER | **Pelecaniformes** |
| FAMILY | **Sulidae** |
| GENUS AND SPECIES | ***Sula leucogaster*** |

WEIGHT
**Male: 1¾–2½ lb. (0.9–1.2 kg); female: 2⅓–3½ lb. (1.1–1.5 kg)**

LENGTH
**Head to tail: 25–29 in. (64–74 cm); wingspan: 52–59 in. (1.3–1.5 m)**

DISTINCTIVE FEATURES
**Powerful, pointed bill; streamlined body; long, tapering wings; webbed feet set far back on body; long tail; dark brown head, upperparts and breast contrast strongly with white underparts**

DIET
**Mainly surface-living, shoaling fish; also prawns and squid**

BREEDING
**Age at first breeding: 2–6 years; breeding season: all year but peaks vary across range; number of eggs: usually 1 or 2; incubation period: 43–47 days; fledging period: 84–119 days; breeding interval: 1 year**

LIFE SPAN
**Up to 22 years**

HABITAT
**Mainly coastal waters, but sometimes flies far from shore; nests on coastal slopes and cliffs**

DISTRIBUTION
**Tropical and warm temperate seas, mainly in Southern Hemisphere**

STATUS
**Generally common, but declining in northern Red Sea**

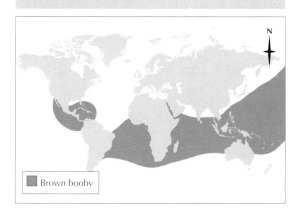

Brown booby

the dive, boobies catch them from underneath while returning to the surface. High-diving is not always employed; boobies occasionally dive from the surface of the sea.

Boobies catch a wide variety of fish, although the Peruvian booby feeds primarily on anchovies. Flying fish are a popular food for all species of booby and are caught not while airborne but just after they have plunged back into the sea after a "flight." Boobies often follow ships, preying on flying fish disturbed by the bow waves.

## Variable breeding

Boobies breed at different times from one year to the next, and so it is not appropriate to talk of a breeding season. Factors influencing the onset of breeding include the prevailing weather and sea conditions. At Ascension Island in the middle of the Atlantic Ocean, where boobies have been studied in detail, the masked booby breeds year-round. However, egg-laying reaches a marked peak in June and July and only a few clutches are started during November, December and January. The brown booby has intense periods of laying only in April and December.

All boobies nest in colonies, with the birds usually crowded together, but nesting sites vary. Masked boobies nest on the flat tops of cliffs, while brown boobies choose more inaccessible places along ledges on cliff faces. Red-footed and Abbott's boobies nest in mangrove trees or bushes and are quite agile in this environment.

## Partners for life

Boobies are slow to form pairs and courtship is prolonged, but once formed pairs stay together for life. Like albatrosses, boobies have an elaborate courtship dance. The male cocks his tail up and goose-steps, lifting his feet as high as possible and puffing out his breast. Sometimes he merely marks time, padding in one place. He then struts up and down, eventually turning toward the female, raising his wings, and emitting a whistle. This is repeated several times, then the strutting continues. At first the female takes little notice of this performance but later she becomes more demonstrative, leaning forward to touch the male's bill or neck.

A booby nest is built of guano (the dried droppings of the boobies themselves), seaweed, feathers and fish bones, which the male collects and deposits in front of the female as she builds up a cup-shaped nest. Two eggs are laid but boobies rarely rear more than one chick. Eggs are sometimes accidentally kicked out of the nest when the incubating bird leaves. However, eggs that a sitting booby can reach with its bill are rolled back into place. Boobies may be found sitting on six or seven eggs that have been retrieved after being knocked out of neighboring nests.

Boobies do not have a brood patch, the area of bare skin on the breast where eggs are kept warm. Instead the webs of their feet develop a rich network of blood vessels that supply heat to the eggs, which are balanced on the feet. Both parents incubate the eggs, taking turns of a few hours each. When not incubating or feeding, boobies congregate with immature birds in groups, known as clubs, outside the breeding colony.

The eggs hatch after 6–7 weeks and the chicks emerge naked and helpless. After 2 weeks the young are covered in a white down, and in 5 months they have grown a full covering of feathers and are ready to take to the air. Unlike juvenile gannets, young boobies are still fed by their parents after they have left the nest, sometimes for as long as 4 months.

## Enemies

Frigate birds and kelp gulls frequently nest near booby colonies and prey on them. The frigate birds also steal boobies' food by chasing them, grabbing their tails and flipping them over. This panics the boobies into disgorging their food, which the frigate birds catch. Kelp gulls raid the booby colonies for eggs and chicks. Sometimes a pair of gulls will work together, one attracting the attention of a sitting booby, drawing it off its nest, while the other sneaks up behind and steals an egg. Peruvian boobies were once heavily exploited by humans for their guano, which was used as a fertilizer.

## Relatives coexist

If two related species are living in the same place they will often eat different foods, and if they eat the same kind of food they will tend to live in different places. In this way species reduce competition for the available food supplies. Where there is an overlap, in food and habitat, one species becomes dominant. It is likely that there is a certain amount of competition between different species of booby. However, habitat and resource division minimizes such competition, allowing similar species to coexist.

Studies of the brown and masked boobies, both of which nest on Ascension Island, show that these closely related birds avoid direct competition for food despite nesting in the same area. Firstly, the ratios of the various fish in their diets vary. The brown booby dives less steeply than the masked booby, penetrating less far into the water, and so feeds mainly on surface-living fish. Furthermore, adult brown boobies spend shorter periods on the nest than masked boobies, since they change over more frequently. The amount of time that an adult has for each fishing trip is therefore more limited, and consequently the feeding grounds of the brown booby are closer inshore than those of the masked booby. Differences in the breeding cycles of brown and masked boobies ensure that the period of their peak food requirements do not coincide. Brown boobies lay eggs mainly in April and December, while masked boobies lay mainly in June and July.

*During its courtship dance the male blue-footed booby paces slowly about with its neck held high. As the display reaches a climax the bird alternately lifts its bright feet, shaking first one and then the other.*

# BOOMSLANG

*Birds have been known to alight on a perfectly camouflaged, motionless boomslang, a mistake they are unlikely to repeat.*

THE BOOMSLANG is one of the rear-fanged snakes in which some of the teeth in the back part of the upper jaw are enlarged and have grooves running down their front surfaces to carry venom. In general, rear-fanged snakes are not dangerous to humans, but the boomslang is an exception to this rule.

Boomslang is a word in the South African language Afrikaans and refers to any tree snake, whereas only one of many tree-living snakes has boomslang as its common English name. This species, *Dispholidus typus*, grows to 6½ feet (2 m) in length, averaging around 5 feet (1.5 m). The body is slender, the tail long, and a distinguishing feature is the rounded, blunt head, which has large eyes with round pupils. The body coloration in males is bright green, sometimes with black patches. Females are almost always a uniform light or dark brown. The variation in color causes boomslangs to be mistaken for other species, especially mambas.

## Agile climber

The boomslang is a very agile snake among trees and bushes, where it slides gracefully through the branches, aided by a prehensile tail. It is able to reach the tips of some of the most slender branches. The boomslang often descends to the ground, however, in search of food or a place to lay its eggs, where it can travel very rapidly, darting back to cover if disturbed. Much of the snake's time is spent immobile, coiled on a branch or, with the help of the prehensile tail, poised with the front part of the body raised in the air. When immobile the boomslang is very difficult to see, its green or brown body merging with the foliage and branches of the tree. Birds, which figure largely in the boomslang's diet, have even been known to perch on them, providing the snake with an easy meal.

## Deadly embrace

The prey of boomslangs is chameleons and other arboreal (tree-dwelling) lizards and snakes, supplemented with birds, small mammals and frogs. An animal is seized in the jaws and held firmly while venom trickles down the grooves in the teeth and acts on the victim. In the case of larger reptiles, the venom takes about 15 minutes to have its effect. This is quite a slow death but the venom is very toxic, only minute quantities being needed to ensure eventual death. In experiments a pigeon was found to succumb after injection with less than 0.0002 mg of boomslang venom.

The boomslang often snatches eggs and fledglings from bird nests, and a boomslang may be mobbed by the furious, if cautious, parents if

# BOOMSLANG

| | |
|---|---|
| CLASS | **Reptilia** |
| ORDER | **Squamata** |
| FAMILY | **Colubridae** |
| GENUS AND SPECIES | ***Dispholidus typus*** |

**LENGTH**
**Up to 6½ ft. (2 m), usually less**

**DISTINCTIVE FEATURES**
**Slender body; large, blunt head; large eyes with round pupils**

**DIET**
**Tree-living snakes and lizards, especially chameleons; also frogs, small mammals and birds, including eggs and nestlings**

**BREEDING**
**Breeding season: spring; number of eggs: up to 25; hatching period: 3–4 months**

**LIFE SPAN**
**Not known**

**HABITAT**
**Trees and bushes, mainly in savanna and other open country**

**DISTRIBUTION**
**Sub-Saharan Africa, except southwest**

**STATUS**
**Locally common**

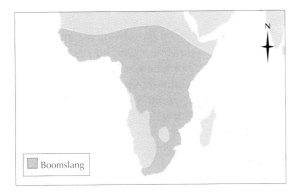

Boomslang

*A boomslang investigates the nest of a pair of masked weavers. Boomslangs are efficient predators of bird eggs and chicks.*

they find it near their nest. Eggs are swallowed whole and the shells dissolved by the snake's strong digestive juices.

## Treetop courtship

Unlike most other snakes, which couple on the ground, boomslangs mate in trees. The eggs, 8 to 25 in number, are laid in early summer, about 4 months after mating. The female seeks out a hollow in which to lay her eggs, perhaps a woodpecker hole in a tree or a hollow in a sandy bank, wherever it is warm and moist. The eggs hatch after 3–4 months, and the newly emerged young measure about 12 inches (30 cm).

## Self-defense

Usually boomslangs retreat from danger but if threatened they will inflate the neck and front part of the body with air, so that it resembles a cobra with its hood inflated. The distention of the body in this manner separates the scales to reveal the brilliantly colored skin that lies between them, alarming most predators. Boomslangs thus have few natural enemies. However, boomslangs are cannibalistic, and one snake is capable of devouring another of nearly the same size.

## Potent poison

Several snakes have been credited with being the most dangerous to humans, notably the cobras (in the genera *Hemachatus*, *Naja* and *Ophiophagus*), mambas (*Dendroaspis*) and kraits (*Bungarus*). It is difficult to find an outright winner in this respect because many factors are involved.

The boomslang is particularly hard to place in a hierarchy of dangerous snakes. Its pure venom is highly toxic, acting both on the nervous system and on the blood system, dissolving the walls of blood vessels and destroying blood cells. The venom is more toxic, weight for weight, than that of mambas and cobras, yet each boomslang secretes only a very small amount. Added to this, boomslangs are shy and bite only if handled. They take some time to inject the venom, having to chew at the wound to allow the venom to penetrate. Nevertheless, one thing is certain. Without access to antidotes and medical aid, and where there is neither knowledge nor medication, boomslang bites can prove fatal.

# BOTTLENOSE DOLPHIN

*Bottlenose dolphins are highly sociable, enjoying the company of their own species. Communal living also affords protection from predators.*

KNOWN BY A VARIETY of names, including common porpoise, this is the marine mammal that has become a star performer in the oceanaria of the United States. It can reach a length of just over 13 feet (4 m) and weighs an average of 660 pounds (300 kg). Its coloration varies greatly, but is usually dark gray on the back and lighter gray on the flanks, lightening further to white or pink on the belly. Older dolphins sometimes have a few spots. The head is bulbous and the beak, or snout, is fairly short but pronounced. The forehead of the male is more protruding than that of the female. The moderate-sized flippers taper to a point and the fin in the middle of the back has a sharply pointed apex directed backward, making the hinder margin concave. There are 40 to 52 teeth in the upper jaw and 36 to 48 teeth in the lower jaw.

As it is a mammal, the bottlenose dolphin gives birth to fully developed young, which are suckled on milk. It occurs virtually worldwide and on the Atlantic coast of North America is the commonest member of the order Cetacea, which includes all the dolphins, porpoises and whales. The bottlenose dolphin can be seen from Florida to Maine, but is most common in the coastal waters of Florida and in the Gulf of Mexico.

## Cooperative schools
Bottlenose dolphins live in groups known as schools, containing individuals of both sexes and all ages. Apparently there is no leader, but males in the school observe a dominance hierarchy based on size. When food is plentiful the schools may be large, breaking into smaller schools when it is scarce. The dolphins pack together at times of danger. They also assist an injured member of the school: one dolphin ranges either side of the weakened animal and, carefully pushing their heads underneath its flippers, raise it to the surface to breathe. In schools the dolphins keep in touch by a variety of calls.

Fish form one of the main items in the dolphins' diet, although a fair amount of cuttlefish, a mollusk, is eaten. The dolphins spit out the chalky cuttlebone inside the cuttlefish and swallow only the soft parts. Shrimps and squid are also eaten. In captivity bottlenose dolphins will consume about 22 pounds (10 kg) of fish a day. They sleep by night and are active by day, although each feeding session is followed by an hour's doze. Females sleep at the surface of the sea with only the blowhole exposed and this periodically opens and closes, as it does in stranded dolphins, by reflex action. The males tend to sleep about 1 foot (30 cm) below the surface, occasionally rising to breathe.

## Adaptations for life underwater
The main swimming action of the bottlenose dolphin is in the tail, with its horizontal flukes. This, the flexible part of the animal, is used with an up-and-down movement quite unlike that of fish, with only an occasional sideways movement. The flippers help in steering and balance. The dorsal fin also aids stability, but it is the lungs, placed high up in the body, that are chiefly responsible for balance.

The depths to which bottlenose dolphins can dive has to be deduced from the remains of fish in their stomachs. Studies of stomach contents show that the dolphins go down for food to at least 70 feet (21 m) below the surface, and that they can stay submerged for up to 15 minutes. Their lung capacity is half as much again as that of a comparable terrestrial mammal and in addition they fill their lungs to capacity. Terrestrial mammals, including humans, use only about half their lung capacity and change only 10–15 percent of the air in the lungs with each breath. A dolphin, however, changes up to 90 percent.

Since a dolphin's lungs are compressed when diving, air would be squeezed into the bronchial tubes, where no gaseous exchange

# BOTTLENOSE DOLPHIN

| | |
|---|---|
| CLASS | **Mammalia** |
| ORDER | **Cetacea** |
| FAMILY | **Delphinidae** |
| GENUS AND SPECIES | ***Tursiops truncatus*** |

ALTERNATIVE NAMES
**Bottle-nosed dolphin; common porpoise; gray porpoise; black porpoise**

WEIGHT
**330–1,435 lb. (150–650 kg), typically 660 lb. (300 kg)**

LENGTH
**Head and body: 6½–13 ft. (2–4 m)**

DISTINCTIVE FEATURES
**Prominent, curved dorsal fin; bulbous head; distinct beak**

DIET
**Fish, especially mullet, eels, anchovies and whiting; also cuttlefish, shrimps and squid**

BREEDING
**Age at first breeding: 10–12 years; breeding season: spring and summer, with peaks March–May and August–September; number of young: 1; gestation period: 360 days; breeding interval: 2–3 years**

LIFE SPAN
**About 25 years**

HABITAT
**Temperate and tropical seas and oceans**

DISTRIBUTION
**Worldwide, except northern Pacific and polar seas**

STATUS
**Common in most of range; relatively abundant in coastal waters of Florida and Gulf of Mexico, but declining in northern Europe, Mediterranean and Black Sea**

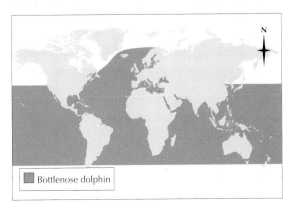

Bottlenose dolphin

would take place, unless this were prevented by valves. There are 25 to 40 of these in the bronchial tubes of the bottlenose dolphin. They act as a series of taps controlling the pressure in the lungs according to whether the animal is diving, rising or swimming on the level.

At the surface the pulse of the bottlenose dolphin is 110 a minute. When submerged it drops to 50 a minute, increasing as the animal nears the surface. The reduction in pulse rate is related to the way the blood circulation is shut off so that the oxygen supply goes mainly to essential organs, notably the heart and brain. This prolongs submergence by reducing the frequency of visits to the surface to breathe.

Whales and dolphins have an insulating layer of blubber, but they have no sweat glands and they cannot pant, so other means are needed to lose excess body heat. The tail flukes and the flippers are always warmer to the touch than the rest of the body and their temperature is not only higher than that of other parts of the body but also varies through a greater range. The flukes and flippers also have a much thinner layer of blubber. It is assumed therefore that these parts lose heat to the surrounding water.

## Senses

A bottlenose dolphin's eyesight is not particularly good. Yet the animal can shut its eyes and even wink. Dolphins in oceanaria will leap out of water and accurately snatch fish from an attendant's hand. Moreover, the visual fields of left and right eyes overlap, so dolphins presumably have partially stereoscopic vision.

The bottlenose dolphin's sense of smell is obviously much reduced due to its aquatic environment and, in common with many whales, it does not have olfactory bulbs. However, it does

*Bottlenose dolphins have excellent hearing, which more than compensates for their poor eyesight.*

*A pair of bottlenose dolphins leaping together in the wild. In oceanaria, dolphins trained to leap out of water have been heard to make sounds to their attendants.*

possess taste buds at the base of the tongue. Captive bottlenose dolphins have been shown to differentiate between different chemicals, in even small concentrations. Other tests suggest that they have only a poor ability to detect salinity and no ability to detect sugar. Dolphin taste buds are possibly used when the animals are in close communication, in a way similar to the operation of pheromones in terrestrial mammals.

After touch and taste, hearing is the main sense in bottlenose dolphins. Their hearing is acute and is especially sensitive to high tones. It is probably second only to the hearing of bats. A dolphin is sensitive to the pulses of an echo sounder and will respond to frequencies as high as 120 kilocycles or beyond, whereas humans can hear 30 kilocycles at the most. At sea it has been noticed that bottlenose dolphins will avoid a boat that has been used for hunting them but will not be disturbed by other boats. The assumption is that the dolphins can recognize individual boats by the sounds they make.

## Slow rate of reproduction

Bottlenose dolphins do not become sexually mature until 10–12 years old. They breed from spring to summer, and the gestation period is around 12 months, with births taking place mainly from March to May. The single young is born tail-first and as soon as it is free it rises to the surface to take a breath, often assisted by the mother, which usually uses her snout to gently lift the baby up. Immediately before the birth the female, or cow, slows down and at the moment of birth she is accompanied by two other cows. These swim one on either side of her, their role

being protective, especially against sharks, which may be attracted to the spot by the smell of blood lost during the birth.

For the first 2 weeks the calf stays close beside the mother, being able to swim rapidly soon after birth. Then it begins to move away and even to chase fish, although quite ineffectively. However, the young dolphin readily dashes back to its mother's side or to its "aunt," the latter being another adult female that attaches herself to the mother and shares in the care of the calf. The aunt is the only dolphin the mother allows near her offspring.

The calf is born with its teeth still embedded in the gums. These begin to erupt in the first weeks of life but the calf makes little attempt to chew until 5 months old, and some take much longer before they attempt to swallow solid food. Suckling takes place underwater. The mother's nipples are small and each lies in a groove on the abdomen. The mother slows down to feed her calf, which comes in behind her and lies slightly to one side, taking a nipple between its tongue and palate. The mother then, by muscular pressure on the mammary glands, squirts the milk into its mouth. Should the calf let go of the nipple, the milk continues to squirt out.

The young bottlenose dolphin must come to the surface to breathe every 30 seconds, so suckling must be rapid. In this species it consists of one to nine sucks, each lasting a few seconds. For the first 2 weeks the calf is suckled about twice an hour, night and day, but by 6 months of age it is down to six feeds a day. The mother lactates for a total of 19 months, and has her next calf 2–3 years after the previous birth.

## Sophisticated communicators

Bottlenose dolphins have a wide vocabulary and much has been learned about the noises they produce. Air can be released from the blowhole while they are still submerged, showing itself as a stream of bubbles. The expulsion of air can be used to make sounds, and part of the mechanism for it is the many small pouches around the blowhole's exit, which serve as safety valves, preventing any inrush of water.

It is known that certain dolphins and whales are attracted over long distances by the calls of fellows in distress. Underwater microphones as well as observations in oceanaria have shown that bottlenose dolphins can produce whistles, squawks, clicks, creaks, quacks and blats, singing notes and wailings. Many of the sounds are in the ultrasonic range and are therefore inaudible to human ears. It has also been found that two dolphins that have been companions will, if separated, call to one another, and that a calf parted from its mother will call to her.

# BOWERBIRD

The male regent bowerbird has a striking plumage, but this is not the main way it attracts a mate. Like other bowerbirds, it impresses females by constructing elaborate shelters called bowers from a wide range of found materials.

THERE ARE 20 SPECIES of bowerbird, found in the forests of Australia and New Guinea. Most bowerbirds favor humid habitats. Some species live in cloud forest, at altitudes of up to 13,100 feet (4,000 m). Others, such as the great gray bowerbird, *Chlamydera nuchalis*, inhabit somewhat drier conditions, such as grasslands and light woodland.

The most studied species is the satin bowerbird, *Ptilonorhnchus violaceus*, of the coastal forests of eastern Australia. The adult male, about 1 foot (30 cm) long, is almost uniformly black, but in sunlight appears lilac blue. The eyes are also blue, though the precise shade varies. Its legs are a dull greenish-yellow and the bill is largely blue with a yellowish tip. The female satin bowerbird is colored quite differently. Its head and back are olive-green, and vary with the light, while the underparts are olive, pale green and yellow. The bill is horn-colored, and the legs and eyes resemble those of the male.

## Bower construction

All young satin bowerbirds have a plumage similar to that of the adult females, but as the young males mature, at 4–6 years, the generally greenish plumage changes to the dark dress of the fully adult males. Before attaining this coloration, the growing males come into breeding condition: that is to say, they mature sexually before becoming adult. They then start making the bowers (dwellings or shelters) that have given these and related birds their name.

The first attempts at bower-building consist of collecting a small number of sticks. Some of these are laid on the ground and others are set vertically. Among the sticks the males place decorative materials. The male satin bowerbird chooses materials that relate in color or texture to his own plumage. However, this correlation is not observed by all species of bowerbird.

There may be 100 or more decorative items selected for the bower. These include natural objects such as feathers, flowers, fungi, insects, wasp nests, the cast skins of snakes and snail shells. Satin bowerbirds and great gray bowerbirds living near human habitation often also collect scraps of artificial materials in the required colors, including paper, rags, broken glass or crockery, milk bottle tops, matchboxes, string, sweet wrappers and similar items. Other bowerbirds tend to collect only natural objects.

The next year's effort shows a considerable advance on the initial construction. Much more material is collected and the bower now comprises a platform of sticks, with a double fence of sticks set vertically in it. The number of decorative objects will also have increased. With the third year, the proportions of the bower increase in all respects. The platform of sticks becomes larger, the palisades (vertical stakes) are longer and thicker and the degree of decoration in the bower is more advanced.

## Instinctive builders

Bower-building mainly follows an innate behavior pattern, but the ability to build takes several years to develop. At some time between April and September, with a peak of building in July, each male occupies a territory and constructs a bower. The actual construction takes a day or two. After this time an area of ground at one end of the bower, the display ground, is decorated with any available colored objects.

At first the main preoccupation of the owner of a bower is to keep other males away. He advertises his presence by flying onto a nearby branch and calling loudly, establishing his claim to the territory. The appearance of a rival male brings the resident bowerbird to the attack. However, the offensive is usually no more than an aggressive display, at which the intruder flees.

## Domestic duties

In due course, a hen is attracted to the bower and there the male displays to her. He picks one of the decorative objects in his bill, lowers his head and stretches his neck, half opens his wings and fans his tail. At the same time he distends his eyes, which may flush a lilac-pink, and makes a rhythmic, whirring song.

The display lasts only a short time, perhaps half a minute or so. The male may hop on stiff legs, run forward, pause or hop sideways, while his wings and tail flick rapidly. Meanwhile, the hen observes his display with little outward reaction. At the most she may utter a few low notes or rearrange a stick in the bower. Should the female move away from the bower, the male ceases his display and calls to her with a special double call, to which she normally responds by returning to her position near to or inside the

*This male great gray bowerbird has adorned his bower with glass, plastic, bones and snail shells.*

## SATIN BOWERBIRD

| | |
|---|---|
| CLASS | **Aves** |
| ORDER | **Passeriformes** |
| FAMILY | **Ptilonorhynchidae** |
| GENUS AND SPECIES | ***Ptilonorhynchus violaceus*** |

ALTERNATIVE NAME
**Satinbird**

LENGTH
**Head to tail: 11–13 in. (27–33 cm)**

DISTINCTIVE FEATURES
**Male: black with deep violet sheen; bluish bill; greenish-yellow legs. Female and young male (up to 4 years): olive-green; pale bill.**

DIET
**Fruits and insects**

BREEDING
**Age at first breeding: up to 6 years; breeding season: October–January; number of eggs: 1 to 3; incubation period: not known; fledging period: not known; breeding interval: 1 year**

LIFE SPAN
**Not known**

HABITAT
**Rain forest and adjacent forest with dense ground cover, eucalypt woodland, orchards, parks and gardens**

DISTRIBUTION
**Eastern Australia**

STATUS
**Fairly common to uncommon**

Satin bowerbird

bower. This is the typical course of events early in the season. Later, under similar circumstances, the male will interrupt his displays and rearrange twigs in the bower with a sliding action of the neck, before following the hen and guiding her back to the bower.

The construction of the bower and its decor is undertaken by the male alone, although the hen may rearrange the twigs while he is displaying or away from the area. It is the hen that builds the nest. She locates it far from the active bower, up to several hundred meters away, generally in the branches of trees. The nests themselves are shallow, concave constructions built of sticks and lined with leaves. Here the female lays one to three eggs, incubating and feeding the chicks unassisted.

## Painting and decorating

In addition to being decorated with colored objects, the walls of the bower may be daubed with various pigments. These may be the juices of colored berries or charcoal from bushfires made into a liquid paste with saliva. A piece of fibrous bark is often used as a swab for dabbing the color onto the sticks of the bower. Not all the satin bowerbird males perform this act, but some do so every day at the height of the breeding season.

Each bowerbird species has its own building methods. Many, including the satin bowerbird and regent bowerbird, *Sericulus chrysocephalus*, construct a so-called avenue bower with parallel walls of sticks or grass enclosing a central avenue, in the form of a pathway of twigs. Others, such as the golden bowerbird, *Prionodura newtoniana*, of northern Queensland in Australia, build what has been termed the maypole bower. This is a vertical mass of twigs built around saplings.

The simplest bower consists of the lower parts of a sapling decorated with twigs, producing an effect similar to that of artificial Christmas trees. Elaborations of this lead to something approaching a wigwam of sticks with a "garden" in front sometimes bounded by a "hedge" of twigs. After the end of the breeding season, the bowers are generally abandoned and fall into disrepair. Rather than remain as settled individuals, the bowerbirds form loose, mobile groups.

## Reasons for the bower

It has been suggested that the male bowerbird's instincts toward bower-building and decoration were once directed toward nest-building and providing food for the young. Over time female bowerbirds have become responsible for these

tasks and the males have redirected their energies accordingly. The bower is thought to act like the male peacock's tail in that it is a signal to a female of the quality of a male. Building a bower takes time and predators may be attracted by both the construction work and the finished product, so only healthy and strong males succeed in making impressive and long-lasting bowers. Moreover, bower-building is a potential sign of good parental care capability, since it indicates a male's ability to provide.

## Feeding habits

Bowerbirds eat mainly fruits and other plant food, such as seeds, leaves, succulent stems and buds. Some species hunt insects, earthworms, spiders and millipedes, while frogs and young birds form a small part of their diets.

Bowerbirds will also eat cultivated fruit and grapes, which has resulted in many being killed by farmers. In certain areas around Melbourne, southern Australia, the satin bowerbird has been virtually exterminated, while the spotted bowerbird, *Chlamydera maculata*, has become almost extinct in the fruit-growing areas of the Murray Valley. However, both species are common elsewhere. Only two species of bowerbird are giving conservationists cause for concern and are considered to be vulnerable: the fire-maned bowerbird, *Sericulus bakeri*, and Archbold's bowerbird, *Archboldia papuensis*.

*Some bowerbirds select objects for their bowers that correspond to their own plumage. This male satin bowerbird has collected blue drinking straws which approximate his own lustrous coloring.*

# BOWFIN

**The bowfin is a rare example of a "living fossil," a species that has not changed since prehistoric times.**

THE BOWFIN IS A living fossil with many primitive features. Its ancestors abounded 130 million years ago, and the single species alive today represents a family and an order of its own. The bowfin is a freshwater fish found only in the waterways of the eastern United States. It inhabits all of the Great Lakes, except Lake Superior, and occurs from the Mississippi River system in Minnesota to the St. Lawrence River in Quebec and down through the Carolinas and Florida as far as the Gulf of Mexico. However, the ancestors of the bowfin were widely distributed over North America and Europe, where their fossils may still be found.

Normally about 2 feet (60 cm) in length, the bowfin may reach 3 feet (91 cm). Long-bodied and pikelike, it has a long, soft-rayed dorsal fin, a rounded tail and thin scales covered with an enamel-like layer called ganoine. The head is covered with bony plates. The male has a dark spot circled with white or orange at the base of the upper tail fin. In females this colored ring, and sometimes the spot itself, is absent. Males are also usually smaller than females.

## Air-breathing fish
The bowfin, sometimes known as the mudfish or spotfin, is unusual for fish in that it can breathe air. It lives in still waters and sluggish streams, and can survive in water with little or no oxygen,

rising to the surface to gulp air. As with several other primitive fish, the swim bladder of the bowfin has a spongy inner lining, well-supplied with blood vessels, that acts as a lung. The bowfin can live out of water for up to 24 hours. It is said to utter a bell-like note, which is possibly caused by exhaling before taking in more air.

Another primitive feature, more pronounced in sharks, is the spiral valve in the intestine. There is only a vestige of this valve in the bowfin, but even that is unusual among the bony or true fish, to which the bowfin belongs. A further feature characteristic of primitive bony fish is the large and bony gular plate on the underside of the head between the two lower jawbones. The bowfin swims mainly by a rapid, wavelike motion of its long dorsal fin.

## Versatile hunter
The bowfin preys on crustaceans, worms, frogs and fish and scavenges dead flesh. It is so voracious and takes such a wide variety of animal foods that where the fish is abundant it is considered destructive and steps are taken to eradicate it. In the southern United States the bowfin is used for food, smoked or dried and in fish balls and jambalaya. Because the bowfin has strong jaws and sharp teeth for tearing apart prey, it has also been called the freshwater dogfish and the freshwater wolf.

# BOWFIN

| | |
|---|---|
| CLASS | **Osteichthyes** |
| SUBCLASS | **Actinopterygii** |
| ORDER | **Amiiformes** |
| FAMILY | **Amiidae** |
| GENUS AND SPECIES | *Amia calva* |

ALTERNATIVE NAMES
**American mudfish; spotfin; freshwater
dogfish; freshwater wolf**

LENGTH
**Up to 3 ft. (91 cm)**

DISTINCTIVE FEATURES
**Long, stout and rounded body; rounded
head; smooth scales; long dorsal fin; bony
plate under throat**

DIET
**Crustaceans, worms, frogs and fish;
also decaying flesh**

BREEDING
**Breeding season: late spring; number of
eggs: 20,000 to 70,000; hatching period:
8–10 days; breeding interval: usually 1 year**

LIFE SPAN
**Up to 12 years**

HABITAT
**Quiet lakes, slow-moving rivers and other
backwaters, often in oxygen-deficient water**

DISTRIBUTION
**Eastern U.S.**

STATUS
**Generally common**

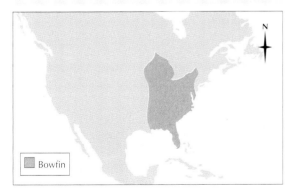

Bowfin spawn in May and June, when the male's dark spot with its ring of color becomes more intense. Firstly the male selects a weedy area along the margin of a lake or stream, often between the roots of trees or among fallen logs. There he builds a circular nest among a clump of water plants. He swims around and around, pressing the vegetation down, much as a bird fashions a nest by pivoting in it, until a saucer-shaped nest is formed.

The courtship ritual begins when a female approaches the nest, and consists of nudges, nose bites and bouts of chasing until she becomes receptive to the male and conception is possible. The female then lies down in the nest, the male takes up a position by her side, and the eggs are laid. Over time, several bowfin couples may use the same nest.

## Guarding the eggs

The male may have a number of different mates and several females may lay their eggs in the nest. After fertilizing the eggs by shedding his milt (sperm-containing fluid) on them, the male guards the nest until the eggs hatch, which occurs in 8–10 days. Sunfish and bass are the primary predators of young bowfin. By swimming around the nest, the guardian male also creates currents that aerate the eggs. Such parental care behavior is clearly an advantage for a species of fish living in sluggish and poorly oxygenated water.

The newly hatched larva is nourished by a large yolk sac. The male guards the young until they are about 4 inches (10 cm) long, when his parental instinct wanes. The young fish have their own protective device in the form of cement glands at the end of the snout. With these organs the young can cling to aquatic vegetation until their rapid growth makes them large and strong enough to swim, at which point they abandon the nest in a compact group with the male in close attendance.

## What is a living fossil?

The bowfin is only one of many animals to have been called a "living fossil." The term is applied to modern species that have not changed since prehistoric times, and was first used by Charles Darwin for a tree, the ginkgo, or maidenhair, *Ginkgo biloba*. The ginkgo tree grew worldwide in Mesozoic times, 200 million years ago, but was thought to have subsequently died out. However, in the 18th century Europeans discovered it to be still surviving in China and Japan.

The large-mouthed predatory fish also appeared during the Mesozoic age, and gave rise to the family to which the bowfin belongs, Amiidae, which originated in the Late Jurassic period, around 150 million years ago. Over the course of the subsequent millennia, the family reached its zenith and declined, the only species left today being the bowfin of the eastern United States. Another species persisted in Europe until 50 million years ago and then died out.

# BREAM

*Bream are mostly silver-gray in color, although their coloring changes according to age and the water they inhabit.*

THE BREAM IS A FRESHWATER FISH of the carp family living in much of Europe as well as western Asia. It is absent from the cooler waters of northern Scandinavia and from the warmer Mediterranean region. The bream is a stocky fish, with a strongly compressed body, high-arched back, especially in older individuals, and small head. The lateral line, instead of following the curve of the back, follows the curve of the belly. Bream grow to about 2 feet (60 cm) in length and can weigh as much as 20 pounds (9 kg), although 10 pounds (4.5 kg) would be considered a large fish.

## Silver fish

The name bream is said to be derived from a Teutonic word meaning to glitter. The flanks of young bream are a gleaming, dull silver color, although the back is a dark blue-gray, and often almost black on older fish. Bream vary in color according to age and water quality.

The same name has been given to another member of the carp family, the white, or silver, bream, *Blicca bjoerkna*, which is similar in habits and appearance to the common bream. The young of the two species are very difficult to tell apart. The adult white bream can be distinguished by, among other features, the red or orange tinge on the paired fins. Some unrelated species of marine fish belonging to the family Sparidae (Porgies) are known as sea bream.

## Sluggish habits

Bream live in shoals and favor warm waters. When about 3 inches (7.5 cm) long they frequent shallow water near the bank in still or slow-moving water, keeping to the bottom. In their second year they move into deep water, shunning the light, hiding in the mud and coming up into shallow water at night to feed. In winter bream rest at the bottom in deep water. They are always sluggish except at spawning time.

The mouth is protractile (capable of being thrust out) and forms a tubelike apparatus when shot out for feeding. Soon after hatching, young bream begin to feed on small plankton but later, when they move into shallow water near the bank, the fish seek bottom-living crustaceans,

# BREAM

| | |
|---|---|
| CLASS | **Osteichthyes** |
| ORDER | **Cypriniformes** |
| FAMILY | **Cyprinidae** |
| GENUS AND SPECIES | ***Abramis brama*** |

ALTERNATIVE NAMES
**Common bream; bream flat (young only)**

WEIGHT
**Usually 2–10 lb. (1–4.5 kg)**

LENGTH
**Up to 2 ft. (60 cm)**

DISTINCTIVE FEATURES
**Stocky, strongly compressed body with high-arched back; small head; mouth protrudes when feeding; long-based anal fin; gleaming silver flanks**

DIET
**Crustaceans, worms, mollusks and insect larvae; occasionally small fish**

BREEDING
**Breeding season: May–June; number of eggs: about 250,000; hatching period: 2–3 weeks**

LIFE SPAN
**Up to 15 years**

HABITAT
**Deep, still fresh waters and sluggish rivers**

DISTRIBUTION
**Much of Europe, and east to western Russia and Kazakhstan**

STATUS
**Very common**

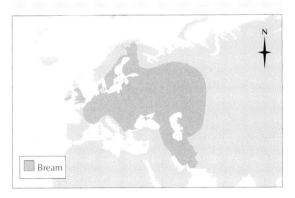

Bream

worms and small mollusks. In their second year, when they have moved to deeper water, they stir up the mud on the bottom with their snouts, feeding on organic matter in the mud and on insect larvae, worms and mollusks. Larger bream eat similar food but also feed on small fish.

## Oldest first

Male and female bream look alike but at spawning time, from May to June, the female, swollen with eggs, appears more robust. The fish come into shallow water, where there is plenty of weedy vegetation. Each female lays about 250,000 eggs, which stick to the leaves and stems of aquatic plants. These normally hatch within 2–3 weeks.

In any one place bream usually spawn in three groups. First to spawn are the oldest and heaviest adults, a week later the medium-sized fish and a week or so after that the smallest adults, which are breeding for the first time. After spawning, all of the adult bream return once more to deep water.

## Muddy refuges

Young bream fall victim to a variety of predatory fish, but as they grow in size their deep bodies afford them a measure of protection from some, such as pike. Their main protection lies, however, in their habit of keeping out of sight in deep water and in burying themselves in the mud. When grubbing at the bottom bream send up clouds of mud and streams of bubbles to the surface. The most vulnerable period for bream, apart from infancy, is the breeding season, when before spawning they come to the surface, rolling and leaping.

## Food fish

In Britain bream are not very popular as a dish. Indeed, river and lake fish, with the exception of salmon, trout and eel, are not widely eaten in Britain. It is said that the flesh of bream has a muddy flavor. However, there is a well-established market for bream in the rest of Europe, and freshwater fish of many species are fully exploited in the developing world. Bream's value as a marketable commodity is considerably enhanced by the fact that it can live for some time out of water, which makes its transportation less problematic than for other fish.

The British are not unusual in failing to take advantage of such a potentially valuable food source. One of the biggest obstacles to making full use of natural food resources all over the world, especially in the case of fish, is prejudice due to fashion. Dogfish under such a name would be unacceptable, but the same food encounters no such stigma when labeled "rock salmon." Redfish, abundant in the North Atlantic but not marketed until the 1960s, is readily eaten, though only under the name of fish fingers.

This whimsical rejection of food sources is one of the problems that has to be faced now and in the future, when considering ways of providing food for increasing human populations.

# BRINE SHRIMP

*In this photograph a male brine shrimp (right) is clasping an egg-laden female (left). Brine shrimps are unusual in that the female's eggs can develop without the male if necessary.*

THE BRINE SHRIMP IS A SMALL AND primitive crustacean found in very salty water in many parts of the world, from Greenland to Australia and from the Caribbean to central Asia. It occurs in both coastal and inland areas, in salt lakes and salt springs and in shallow ponds where seawater has evaporated to produce a highly concentrated salt solution. Countries and regions with high populations of brine shrimps include North America, Venezuela, Argentina, North Africa, Spain, Russia, India and Australia. In the United States, brine shrimps are particularly abundant in Arizona, California, Nebraska, North Dakota, New Mexico and Utah.

Although most of the shrimps are less than ½ inches (13 mm) long, they may be so numerous as to color the water red. This is due to the red, oxygen-carrying pigment, hemoglobin, which the shrimps contain.

## Seeing and eating

A brine shrimp has two pairs of antennae, two compound eyes (eyes made of many separate visual units, such as the eyes of insects) on stalks, and a third, small eye in the middle of its head. It has 11 pairs of rhythmically beating limbs with which it swims upside down, or rather with its ventral (lower) surface to the light, because the shrimp will turn over if illuminated from below.

The physical appearance of the animal varies a little according to the amount of salt in the water in which it lives. There are many species and strains of brine shrimp throughout the world, although *Artemesia salina* is the best known.

The brine shrimp feeds on tiny particles of organic matter suspended in the water through which it swims. The rippling motion of the flattened limbs, each one-sixth of a beat ahead of the pair in front, sweeps the particles in currents of water backward along the front of the body. The particles are caught in strainers formed by the bristles on the inner edges of the limbs and are thence transferred forward to the mouth.

## Dormant eggs survive drought

During reproduction the male brine shrimps clasp the females by means of specially modified antennae. The females have a brood pouch attached to their bodies behind the limbs, where the larvae remain for some time before being liberated when conditions are favorable to their survival. The young are active, with short bodies and no limbs but large antennae, which are used for swimming. These so-called nauplius larvae become adults after a succession of molts and, in a warm room, become mature in about 3 weeks. Some shrimp colonies consist of females only and in these the eggs develop without being fertilized, a process known as parthenogenesis.

Sometimes, as a result of mating and not parthenogenesis, eggs are laid that may either hatch very soon or lie inactive for long periods. Such resting eggs have hard brown shells and can be dried and kept for years before being hatched in salt water. Since many of the ponds and lakes in which brine shrimps live owe their extreme saltiness to the evaporation of water, and may dry up completely, the value of an egg that can survive the complete disappearance of water is obvious.

The potential longevity of the eggs is very convenient for aquarists, who use brine shrimps as fish food. They buy the dry eggs and hatch out the larvae, rearing them to adulthood in seawater on a diet of yeast. The eggs they buy are packaged in various parts of North America, especially around the Great Salt Lake in Utah, where they are superabundant. Many commercial fish farms could not survive without brine shrimps to feed to the larval fish in their care. In North Africa the eggs of brine shrimps are made into a paste and eaten with dates.

## BRINE SHRIMPS

| | |
|---|---|
| PHYLUM | **Arthropoda** |
| CLASS | **Crustacea** |
| SUBCLASS | **Branchiopoda** |
| ORDER | **Anostraca** |
| GENUS | ***Artemia*** |
| SPECIES | **Many, including *A. salina*** |

LENGTH
**Up to about ½ in. (13 mm)**

DISTINCTIVE FEATURES
**11 pairs of rhythmically beating legs; 2 pairs of antennae; 2 compound eyes on stalks; reddish coloration**

DIET
**Planktonic particles, especially algae**

BREEDING
**Larval period: about 21 days; breeding interval: many generations per year**

LIFE SPAN
**A few weeks or months**

HABITAT
**Highly saline water, including salt springs, salt lakes and salt pans**

DISTRIBUTION
**Worldwide in water of 43–95° F (6–35° C); absent from polar areas and very cold temperate regions**

STATUS
**Superabundant**

*Brine shrimps favor waters with a high salt content, such as the Great Salt Lake in Utah (above).*

### Life beyond boiling point

It is remarkable enough that the resting eggs should be able to survive for years when dried out, but this is not the limit of their tolerance. By drying the eggs in a high vacuum, practically every trace of water can be removed and the chemical processes of life can be brought to a complete standstill. If such dried eggs are cooled to the temperature of liquid air, around -310° F (-190° C), they will still hatch when returned to salt water at a normal temperature. Moreover, provided they are fully dry, a small proportion will even endure for 2 hours at a temperature of 221° F (105° C). To be boiled and survive is a remarkable characteristic.

Adult brine shrimps are also unusual in their tolerance of harsh conditions, but in a different way. They can be found in water so full of salt that crystals form around the edge of the pool.

Such water can contain about 30 percent of salt as compared with the 3.5 percent present in the sea. In the laboratory, brine shrimps can also survive in seawater diluted to only a tenth of its normal strength. However, although they are perfectly able to live in the sea, they do not do so and in nature live only in water that is more than twice as salty, such as in salt pans and salt springs. The reason seems to be that brine shrimps would be very vulnerable to many kinds of predators in the sea and that they can only flourish in water too concentrated for these potential enemies to survive in. Thus the shrimps are literally preserved in brine.

### Balancing act

One major problem that faces all animals living in water containing concentrations of salts different from those in their body fluids is that of preserving a proper internal balance of water and salts. This is because the concentrations of each constituent in the body tend always to equalize with those outside. An animal living in freshwater has to prevent the salts from leaking out of its body. By contrast, one living in concentrated salt solutions has to prevent too many salts flooding into its body, thus destroying its internal balance.

The brine shrimp has to ensure that its internal salt concentration is kept lower than that of the surrounding brine, as low indeed as that of a freshwater animal. The shrimp does this by absorbing salty water from its alimentary canal and expelling the surplus salt through special gill areas on its limbs. It is vital for the shrimp to dedicate its energies to this task. However, it need expend correspondingly far less effort on escaping predators, few of which can survive in the brine shrimp's rigorous environment.

# BRISTLEMOUTH

*Bristlemouths look extraordinary due to the light-emitting organs on their flanks. They have poor eyesight, however, and so probably hunt using smell and by detecting movement in the water.*

B RISTLEMOUTHS ARE ALMOST certainly the most common fish anywhere in the world. The species *Cyclothone microdon* is the most super-abundant of all. Together with lantern fish and hatchet fish, bristlemouths form the so-called Lilliputian fauna of the deep sea, which represents 90 percent of all the deeper-dwelling oceanic fish preying on small planktonic animals. There are between 400 and 500 bristlemouths to the pound (0.5 kg).

The eyes of bristlemouths are small and rows of small light-emitting organs called photophores lie along their flanks. Some species are black and dark brown, others pale-colored, depending on the depths at which they live.

## Gaping mouths

Many bathypelagic, or deep-sea, fish have mouths with very large gapes, an adaptation to making the most of the few food resources available at such depths. Bristlemouths are no exception and can open their mouths, which are armed with bristlelike teeth, through nearly 180°. They feed on small planktonic animals, such as copepods, amphipods and pteropods (sea butterflies). Prey is picked off as the bristlemouths drift by.

## Life in the dark

When a light-sensitive tube is lowered into the ocean, flashes of light can be detected to depths of up to 13,000 feet (4,000 m), whereas the penetration of sunlight ceases at depths of 1,500–1,800 feet (460–550 m). The flashes of light come from the light-emitting organs of deep-sea animals. But the light is intermittent and sporadic and would provide a poor target for feeding fish. It is now generally understood that deep-sea fish can detect the sources of odors and disturbances through the nose and the lateral line organs.

## BRISTLEMOUTHS

| CLASS | **Osteichthyes** |
|---|---|
| ORDER | **Stomiiformes** |
| FAMILY | **Gonostomatidae** |
| GENUS | ***Cyclothone*** |
| SPECIES | ***C. microdon; C. pallida;* many others** |

ALTERNATIVE NAME
**Lightfish**

WEIGHT
**Probably up to ¹/₁₀ oz. (2 g)**

LENGTH
**1½–3 in. (3.5–8 cm)**

DISTINCTIVE FEATURES
**1 or more rows of photophores along body (absent in 12 species); small eyes**

DIET
**Small copepods, amphipods and pteropods**

BREEDING
**Poorly known. Number of eggs: 1,000 (Mediterranean) to 10,000 (North Atlantic).**

LIFE SPAN
**Not known**

HABITAT
**Deepest layer of seas and oceans, 650–8,850 ft. (200–2,700 m) below surface**

DISTRIBUTION
**All marine environments, including Arctic and Antarctic waters (*C. microdon*)**

STATUS
**World's most abundant fish**

Presumably, therefore, bristlemouths do not hunt by sight, but by smell or by picking up minute vibrations in the water.

Male bristlemouths have a highly developed olfactory (smell) organ, but females do not, which suggests that males also use this organ to locate a mate. The eggs are laid in deep waters and then float to the surface layers, where they hatch. The larvae are massed in the upper waters throughout spring and summer, where the density of plankton is greatest. Adolescents and adults occupy different levels in the sea, thus avoiding competition for plankton.

# BRISTLETAIL

## BRISTLETAILS

| | |
|---|---|
| PHYLUM | **Arthropoda** |
| CLASS | **Insecta** |
| ORDER | **Thysanura** |
| FAMILY | **Lepismatidae** |
| GENUS | ***Lepisma, Thermobia, Ctenolepisma, Campodea, Peliolepisma* and possibly others** |
| SPECIES | **Up to 550, including silverfish, *Lepisma saccharina*; firebrat, *Thermobia domestica*; four-lined silverfish, *Cteno-lepisma quadriseriata*; and long-tailed silverfish, *C. longicaudata*** |

*This two-pronged bristletail belongs to the genus* Campodea. *When viewed from above, bristletails have a much less distinct head, thorax and abdomen than most other insects.*

BRISTLETAILS LIVE throughout the world and are thought to be among the most primitive insects alive today. The silverfish, *Lepisma saccharina*, is one of the best-known species and is found in bread bins, kitchens and cupboards and among books. Bristletails get their name from two or three slender, bristlelike "tails" located at the rear of the body. They have small compound eyes, two long antennae and long, slender legs that are well adapted for running. No bristletail is longer than ¾ inches (2 cm) overall.

## Primitive nocturnal scavengers

Bristletails move swiftly, with a wriggling motion that resembles the swimming action of fish. Most bristletails live in damp, sheltered places, such as under stones and logs, among leaf litter and beneath dead bark. Some live in the nests of ants and termites. Others may inhabit warm, humid places. Bristletails come out mainly at night, and this nocturnal habit, combined with their small size and neutrally colored, slender bodies, means they are seldom seen. Those most commonly seen are two species that have taken to living in houses: the silverfish, already mentioned, and the firebrat, so named because it lives around fireplaces, boilers and flues.

Bristletails are thought to prefer starchy foods but will eat almost anything, including pieces of dead plant and plant products, wallpaper paste, glue, bookbindings, paper, photographs and dead insects. They can go without food for as long as a year if necessary.

The female silverfish lays more than 100 eggs in her lifetime. These are deposited singly or in small groups in secluded places. The minute eggs, which are very hard to find, are laid freely

**LENGTH**
**Up to ¾ in. (2 cm)**

**DISTINCTIVE FEATURES**
**Wingless; slender, carrot-shaped body; 2 or 3 long, bristlelike tail filaments; 2 long antennae. Firebrat: gray or brown body with dark specks. Silverfish: shiny silver scales.**

**DIET**
**Almost anything, including plant matter, dead insects, human foodstuffs, fabrics, paper, books, wallpaper paste and glue**

**BREEDING**
**Number of eggs: (silverfish) 100 or more during lifetime; (firebrat) up to 50 in each of several batches; hatching period: 6–60 days**

**LIFE SPAN**
**Adult: 2–8 years**

**HABITAT**
**Silverfish: cool, damp places. Firebrat: warm, humid places. Some species live inside ant or termite nests.**

**DISTRIBUTION**
**Worldwide**

**STATUS**
**Abundant, but populations increase slowly**

on the ground and in cracks and crevices, although the choice of egg-laying location probably depends on species and habitat. The eggs hatch in 6–60 days, depending on temperature. Young, immature silverfish, known as nymphs, are white and lack scales but acquire the adult coloring within 4–6 weeks.

# BRITTLE STAR

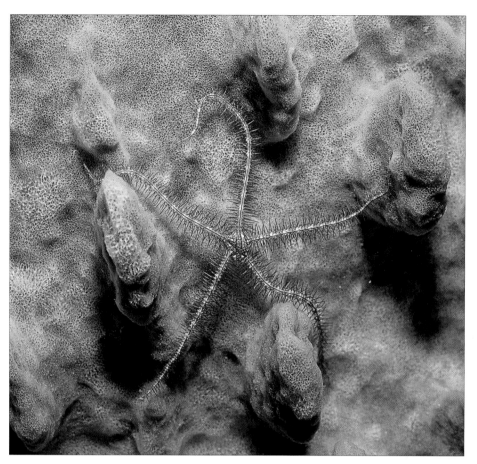

*Brittle stars can travel at speeds of 6 feet per minute (1.8 m/min). This is quite fast compared with the slow crawling of other echinoderms, such as starfish and urchins, that drift along on their tube feet.*

Brittle stars are found in seas all over the world, from the tideline to deep water and from the poles to the Tropics. Many species of brittle star live on the seabed, burrowing into it if it is muddy. Others live among seaweed and corals, climbing around the fronds by grasping them with their flexible arms. On the seabed brittle stars move by waving the arms in a rowing action. Either two or four arms work together in pairs. The fifth is held out in front or trails behind, sometimes assisting in the motion by a beating action.

## Two ways of feeding

Brittle stars have two basic feeding methods. They capture small particles on the arms and pass these to the mouth, which lies on the underside of the disk, and they tear off lumps of dead flesh and seaweed with the tube feet and teeth around the mouth.

Organic debris in the mud and floating in suspension, as well as minute planktonic animals and plants, are trapped on the arms by numerous fine, sticky spines, or by strings of mucus. The skin around the arms is covered with cilia, which sweep the mucus and entrapped particles toward the tube feet on the underside of the arms. The tube feet also help in this movement by "licking" around the parts of the arm within reach. In this way they become covered in a mixture of mucus and particles. The mixture is wiped off against a spine near each tube foot and the resulting mass transferred on the tip of the tube foot to another nearer the mouth. As the mass is moved inward, more is added and it is patted by the tube feet to form a compact ball. Eventually the ball is brought to the root of the arm, where it is transferred to tube feet around the mouth for tasting. If the material is acceptable, it is forced into the mouth. If it is not, it is passed back down the arm and released.

Brittle stars also feed on larger animals and carrion. Lumps of food up to 1 inch (2.5 cm) across are caught, wrapped in an arm and held by the tube feet. The arm then curves over to carry the food to the mouth. Smaller pieces of food are grasped by the arm, then transferred along it by the tube feet in the same way as the mucous ball. Brittle stars can detect the presence of food, provided it lies upstream, presumably by sensing chemicals released from the food. The

Brittle stars are echinoderms closely related to basket stars and more distantly to starfish. Like the latter, brittle stars have five arms joined to a central body, although more arms are present in a few species. The body, or disk as it is known, is button-shaped, and the arms are snakelike. The English name alludes to the ease with which the arms fall off, although arms that become detached are regrown.

There are more than 1,800 known species of brittle star. Some are a light gray in color but many are delicately colored. The largest brittle stars have disks of 4 inches (10 cm) in diameter with a spread of 2 feet (60 cm) across the arms. Another species has a disc only 0.5 mm across.

## Submarine acrobats

The arms of brittle stars are covered with many rows of hard plates and spines, while running down the center of each arm are vertebrae that form a flexible structure a little like the backbone in mammals. Muscles controlling movement are attached to these vertebrae. Along the underside of the arms are rows of tube feet, called podia. The tube feet are used for feeding, whereas similar structures in starfish are used for walking.

# BRITTLE STARS

| | |
|---|---|
| PHYLUM | **Echinodermata** |
| CLASS | **Ophiuroidea** |
| ORDER | **Ophiurae** |
| GENUS | **Many, including *Amphiura*, *Ophiura* and *Ophiothrix*** |
| SPECIES | **More than 1,800** |

**LENGTH**
**Arm spread: up to 2 ft. (60 cm); diameter of central disc: up to 4 in. (10 cm)**

**DISTINCTIVE FEATURES**
**Usually 5 narrow, spiny arms radiating from central disc; more in some species**

**DIET**
**Small particles filtered from water; some species scavenge dead organisms**

**BREEDING**
**Age at first breeding: 1 year; some species hermaphrodites; planktonic stage: usually several weeks**

**LIFE SPAN**
**Usually 1–5 years, more in some species**

**HABITAT**
**Most marine habitats, including in deep-sea mud, under shoreline stones and in seaweed**

**DISTRIBUTION**
**Worldwide, from intertidal zone to deep sea**

**STATUS**
**Many species superabundant**

arms wave about, then, having determined in which direction the food lies, the brittle star moves toward its target.

## Simple sexual organs

In most species of brittle stars, eggs and sperm are merely shed into the sea, where fertilization takes place. The sexual organs are therefore very simple. There are genital openings at the base of each arm through which the sex cells are discharged. There may, however, be a bag, or bursa, just inside the opening, into which the cells are discharged from the gonads.

The fertilized eggs develop into delicate larvae with long arms, stiffened with fine rods, and covered with cilia that beat to keep the larva from sinking. The larva, called an ophiopluteus, drifts for some time, eventually developing into the adult, after which it settles on the seabed.

A few brittle stars do not have free-swimming larvae but retain their eggs in the bursae or in the ovaries, where they develop into small adults before crawling out through the genital slits. These species are often hermaphrodites, having both male and female sex organs, but they avoid self-fertilization because the cells of one sex ripen before the other.

## Defensive measures

Many brittle stars fall prey to bottom-feeding fish, especially plaice and dab. The species that burrow into mud manage to avoid predation to some extent, but still risk having their arms bitten off. Some species have evolved more advanced forms of defense. These brittle stars have light-producing cells on the spines of the arms. When one arm is bitten off, the others produce a flash of light. This display appears to deter the predator from following up the attack, and may even prevent it from attacking other brittle stars in the future.

## Brittle stars cling together

Around the shores of the eastern coast of the United States there is a brittle star that normally lives among the stems of eelgrass, hanging onto them by its arms. In winter the eelgrass dies back and the brittle stars twine their arms around one another to form a tight bunch. When curled around an object, a brittle star is exerting tension, which increases the rate of its body functions. For some reason that is not properly understood, this enables them to live longer than brittle stars that live in isolation. They are also less likely to lose their arms. Therefore it is an advantage to cling to any object, so, without the normal solid supports, they cling to one another.

*Collecting small particles is a passive method of feeding. Brittle stars rest on the seabed or burrow down into the mud, leaving only arms exposed, which wave about in the water.*

# BROADBILL

Broadbills live mainly in humid jungles and evergreen and semievergreen forests in the Tropics. They are particularly widespread in secondary forests where virgin jungle has been burned down, cultivated, then allowed to grow again. A few species live in mangrove swamps, gardens and fields. Most are found in Southeast Asia, from the Himalayan foothills to Borneo. There are also some species in Africa, south of the Sahara Desert. Only two broadbills favor mountain forests as a habitat.

## Jungle life

Broadbills are gregarious and well known for their unusual tameness, tending to stay still rather than fly when alarmed. Some species live near the ground while others frequent the treetops, working through the forest in small flocks of up to 20, exploring branches and creepers, climbing about them like tiny parrots and continually calling and whistling to one another. A few species, such as the green broadbills, are solitary and much quieter.

Many broadbills are insect-eaters, probing into bark or pulling insects out of crevices. Flying insects are caught on the wing. The long-tailed broadbill feeds on large moths, stick insects and similar creatures, and the larger broadbills will take small lizards and frogs. The green broadbills eat mainly fruits.

## Courtship and nesting

At the beginning of the breeding season the small flocks of broadbills separate into pairs. Several species have elaborate courtship displays and there is a variety of songs within the family. The red-sided broadbill, *Smithorius rufolateralis*, of Africa is called "cock of the forest" by the Congolese because it is the first bird to start singing in the morning.

The red-sided broadbill makes short flights in a circle, only a foot or two in diameter, just above its perch. During this flight the bright red patches under the wings are displayed to attract the female, while a klaxonlike croak is made by beating the stiff wing feathers. Other species of broadbill also make noises with their wings, or have musical, whistling songs.

A broadbill nest is a huge, elaborate structure hanging from a branch, often over water. It is a pear-shaped mass of dead leaves, grasses, sticks and fibers, 5–6 feet (1.5–2 m) long and hanging about 10 feet (3 m) above the ground, the height depending on the species. The main bulk of the nest, hung by a thin rope of

*A nesting pair of black-and-red broadbills,* Cymbirhychus macrorhynchus, *in Borneo, Malaysia. Building the nest is a community effort.*

THE BROADBILLS ARE 15 SPECIES of brightly colored forest birds, usually with silky, green or blue plumage. They are plump, 5–11 inches (13–28 cm) in length, with short legs and wide, hooked bills. Three species of broadbill, all of which are bright green, appear to have minute bills, but this is because their bills are almost entirely covered with a dense tuft of small, fine feathers. The long-tailed broadbill, *Psarisomus dalhousiae,* has a green body with a black and yellow head and blue on the crown, wings and tail. Female and young broadbills resemble adults, but are duller in color than adult males.

# GRAUER'S BROADBILL

| | |
|---|---|
| CLASS | **Aves** |
| ORDER | **Passeriformes** |
| FAMILY | **Eurylaimidae** |
| GENUS AND SPECIES | ***Pseudocalyptomena graueri*** |

ALTERNATIVE NAMES
**Green broadbill; African green broadbill**

WEIGHT
**1–1¼ oz. (29–35 g)**

LENGTH
**Head to tail: about 5 in. (13 cm)**

DISTINCTIVE FEATURES
**Mainly green plumage, with blue ear coverts, chin, throat and upper breast**

DIET
**Seeds, flowers, fruits, beetles and snails**

BREEDING
**Breeding season: April–August; number of eggs: 3 to 5; incubation period: not known; fledging period: not known**

LIFE SPAN
**Not known**

HABITAT
**Primary rain forest edge, at altitude of 6,200–7,900 ft. (1,900–2,400 m)**

DISTRIBUTION
**Easternmost Congo (formerly Zaire) east to to parts of western Uganda**

STATUS
**Not known**

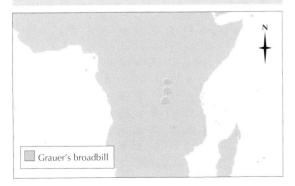

Grauer's broadbill

As is usual with birds of dense tropical forests, little is known of the breeding habits of broadbills. They may lay two to eight eggs, but a clutch of three to five eggs is thought to be more common. These are white or pinkish with a varying amount of purplish or red spotting. The length of the incubation period and the share taken by each sex remain unclear, but both parents have been seen feeding the young.

*Most broadbills have a bright plumage, and the male blue-crested broadbill, Mylagra azureocapilla, of Fiji in the southern Pacific, is no exception.*

## Reclusive species

Not only is the behavior of jungle birds poorly understood, but in some cases the bird itself is hardly ever seen, for even common species may escape detection if they are secretive. One species of broadbill was for many years known to science from just 12 specimens.

The broadbill in question was first found by a collector called Rudolf Grauer in a bamboo forest north of Lake Tanganyika, East Africa. In 1909 Lord Rothschild published a description of the bird, calling it *Pseudocalyptomena graueri*. His description attracted considerable interest in the ornithological world because, previously, broadbills were not thought to exist in Africa.

Another 20 years passed before Grauer's broadbill was seen again. Eventually Alan Moses, a member of an American expedition, tried to find the species in the bamboo forests of central Africa. After much searching he located a bird to the north of the original site. It was mostly green in color with blue ear coverts, a blue chin and upper breast. Grauer's broadbill has since been recorded from a handful of locations in Uganda and the Democratic Republic of the Congo.

fibers and grasses, is intricately woven with an entrance in one side near the bottom. Mosses and lichens decorate the exterior. Both sexes help in building the nest and in the dusky broadbill, *Corydon sumatranus,* as many as 10 individuals have been seen working together.

# BROW-ANTLERED DEER

**Fewer than 100 of the critically endangered Manipur subspecies of brow-antlered deer survive in the wild.**

(115 kg). It is now so rare that its survival is giving cause for concern. The population was estimated to have fallen to about 100 in the 1970s, and it is now confined to the southwestern part of Lake Logtak in Manipur state, India. Another subspecies, *C. e. siamensis,* was formerly abundant from southern Thailand and Cambodia through Laos and Vietnam to the Hainan Islands. Its populations are now greatly reduced in all areas except for parts of Cambodia. The third subspecies, *C. e. thamin,* of lower Burma and Tenasserim, is not at present in danger of extinction.

## Swamp-dwellers

Male brow-antlered deer are usually loners, but females associate in herds of 10 to 50 individuals. When the species was more plentiful, herds of 200 or 300 were frequently seen. They inhabit low-lying, swampy ground and, although they may enter the fringe of the forest for shade during the day, generally keep to the open. Brow-antlered deer are mainly grazers, feeding on wild rice and other plants growing in the swamps, but they also browse certain trees. The does utter short, barking grunts, while the call of the stags is a more prolonged grunt.

THE RARE BROW-ANTLERED DEER of southern Asia has most unusual antlers. A unique form of antler is carried by the stags (males) in which the brow tine curves down over the forehead to form an almost continuous sweep with the beam. The beam is curved first backward and outward then slightly forward, after which it divides into a short fork, of which the two prongs may split up into as many as 10 points. There are usually one or more prominent snags at the junction of the brow tine with the beam. An average set of antlers measures about 40 inches (1 m) from the tip of the brow tine along the curve to the extremity.

In winter the stag's coat is coarse and shaggy, dark brown above and whitish below, sometimes with a white mark above the eye. This changes in summer to reddish-brown with pale brown underparts. The females, or does, remain a paler rufous fawn throughout the year. Young fawns are spotted with white.

There are three subspecies of brow-antlered deer, distinguished mainly by differences in antler construction. The Manipur brow-antlered deer, *Cervus eldi eldi,* stands about 4 feet (1.2 m) at the shoulder and weighs up to 250 pounds

The hooves of the Manipur subspecies are adapted to the special conditions of its habitat and are unlike those of the other two subspecies. Its pasterns (the lower part of the legs) are horny and greatly elongated to help the animal in moving over the dense mass of vegetation known as *phundi* that carpets the surface of Lake Logtak. The *phundi* is a floating mat of dead or decaying organic matter on which reeds, grasses and other vegetation grow. It varies in thickness from a few inches to several feet. When crossing it the deer has been described as appearing to proceed on its hind legs, the body being held almost vertical. During the rainy season, when much of the surrounding country is flooded, the weight of the water causes the *phundi* to sink deeper into the lake, and at this time the deer leave the lake for drier areas and may wander considerable distances. As soon as the vegetation on the lake dries out and rises higher in the water, the deer return.

During the rutting season much fighting goes on between the stags, sometimes resulting in a stag losing one or both eyes. It has been

# BROW-ANTLERED DEER

| | |
|---|---|
| CLASS | **Mammalia** |
| ORDER | **Artiodactyla** |
| FAMILY | **Cervidae** |
| GENUS AND SPECIES | *Cervus eldi* |

ALTERNATIVE NAMES
**Thamin; Eld's deer; Manipur brow-antlered deer (*C. eldi eldi* only)**

WEIGHT
**210–330 lb. (95–150 kg)**

LENGTH
**Head and body: 59–67 in. (1.5–1.7 m); shoulder height: 47–51 in. (1.2–1.3 m); tail: 9–10 in. (23–25 cm)**

DISTINCTIVE FEATURES
**Male has unique antler shape**

DIET
**Wild rice and other grasses; also herbs, twigs and fruits**

BREEDING
**Age at first breeding: 1–2 years; breeding season: February–May; gestation period: about 242 days; number of young: 1; breeding interval: 1 year**

LIFESPAN
**Up to 19 years in captivity**

HABITAT
**Low-lying swamps and forest margins, sometimes in drier, grassy areas; avoids dense vegetation**

DISTRIBUTION
**Scattered populations: Assam in northeastern India, Myanmar (Burma), Thailand, Laos, Cambodia and Vietnam**

STATUS
**Critically endangered: *C. eldi eldi*; vulnerable: *C. eldi siamensis* and *C. eldi thamin***

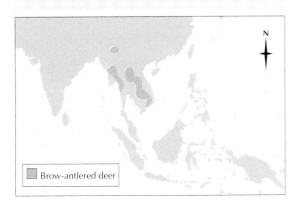

Brow-antlered deer

noticed that totally blind stags survive as long as they keep with a herd, their acute hearing informing them of the herd's movements, but once they lose the herd they soon fall victim to hunters or to animal predators.

Although tigers and leopards prey on the brow-antlered deer its chief enemy has always been humans. The animal has been hunted for its antlers and by local people for its flesh. The Manipur subspecies is facing extinction mainly because of indiscriminate shooting, particularly when the deer are driven out of their usual environment by flooding and move to higher, more open ground. The deer has been legally protected since 1934, but it is not always easy to enforce the protective measures. A few are kept in zoos, but they do not thrive in captivity.

## Known only by its antlers

There is the chance that the brow-antlered deer may yet suffer the fate of a closely related Southeast Asian species called Schomburgk's deer. This deer appears to have become extinct at some time between 1932 and 1939, and has never been seen alive by Europeans.

Knowledge of Schomburgk's deer is limited to surviving sets of antlers and to stories told by local Thai people who hunted the deer and sold its antlers in local markets. It was said to stand 42 inches (105 cm) high at the shoulder and be rich brown above and white below, but its outstanding feature was magnificent antlers. These were remarkable for the number and complexity of their many points, or prongs. During the breeding season, when the stag used his antlers to wrestle with other stags in the forest, it was said that the clashing of the prongs could be clearly heard in distant villages.

*Male brow-antlered deer tend to be solitary, whereas the females (above) live in small groups.*

# Index

Page numbers in *italics* refer to picture captions.
Index entries in **bold** refer to guidepost or biome and habitat articles.

Page numbers in *italics* refer to picture captions. Index entries in **bold** refer to guidepost or biome and habitat articles.